SCHIZOPHRENIA

Publication Number 536

AMERICAN LECTURE SERIES®

A Monograph in

AMERICAN LECTURES IN LIVING CHEMISTRY

Edited by

I. NEWTON KUGELMASS, M.D., PH.D., Sc.D.

*Consultant to the Departments of Health and Hospitals
New York, New York*

SCHIZOPHRENIA

Chemistry, Metabolism and Treatment

By

J. R. SMYTHIES, M.Sc., M.D., M.R.C.P., D.P.M.

Senior Lecturer, Department of Psychological Medicine
University of Edinburgh
Consultant Psychiatrist
Royal Edinburgh Hospital
Edinburgh, Scotland

CHARLES C THOMAS • PUBLISHER

Springfield • Illinois • U.S.A.

1/1972
Psych.

Published and Distributed Throughout the World by
CHARLES C THOMAS • PUBLISHER
BANNERSTONE HOUSE
301-327 East Lawrence Avenue, Springfield, Illinois, U.S.A.

© *1963, by* CHARLES C THOMAS • PUBLISHER
Library of Congress Catalog Card Number: 62-21328

With THOMAS BOOKS careful attention is given to all details of manufacturing and design. It is the Publisher's desire to present books that are satisfactory as to their physical qualities and artistic possibilities and appropriate for their particular use. THOMAS BOOKS will be true to those laws of quality that assure a good name and good will.

Printed in the United States of America

To Vanna

FOREWORD

OUR Living Chemistry Series was conceived by Editor and Publisher to advance the newer knowledge of chemical medicine in the cause of clinical practice. The interdependence of chemistry and medicine is so great that physicians are turning to chemistry, and chemists to medicine in order to understand the underlying basis of life processes in health and disease. Once chemical truths, proofs and convictions become sound foundations for clinical phenomena, key hybrid investigators clarify the bewildering panorama of biochemical progress for application in everyday practice, stimulation of experimental research, and extension of postgraduate instruction. Each of our monographs thus unravels the chemical mechanisms and clinical management of many diseases that have remained relatively static in the minds of medical men for three thousand years. Our new Series is charged with the *nisus élan* of chemical wisdom, supreme in choice of international authors, optimal in standards of chemical scholarship, provocative in imagination for experimental research, comprehensive in discussions of scientific medicine, and authoritative in chemical perspective of human disorders.

Dr. Smythies of Edinburgh presents the current concept of schizophrenia as a dynamic process conditioned by genetic forces and triggered by environmental excitants. It flays the mind and leaves the body whole but appears potentially reversible in both acute and chronic types of reaction. The degree of impairment in personality functioning varies directly with the duration of specific distortions in thought, feeling, volition, and behavior. There is not a sight in Nature so mortifying as that of a troubled mind, disordered psyche, and confused spirit. Babylon in all its desolation is not so melancholy a spectacle as that of the human mind in ruins. The world abounds in this tragic disorder of the regressed individual as a social unit attempting emergency adaptations to the overload of life: Homo sum; humani nil a me alienum puto.

Horace (25 B.C.) revealed: Cocea insanire omnes. No man is quite sane. Each has a vein of folly in his composition that holds him hard to a deed which he has taken to heart. The ancients taught that there was one kind of common sense and many varieties of lunacy. Those who espoused the former were considered normal, and the latter abnormal fit for incarceration in asylums. Psychiatry was thus concerned with custodial care and clinical classification and remained a discipline remote from medicine and from every-day life. Such isolation was the sum-total of wretchedness to man and degradation to medicine. To olden tenets of maintenance regimentation and mental philosophy gradually gave way to the holistic approach of understanding the total organism in his social milieu. We now have reason to believe that the most incomprehensible thing about the human brain is that it is comprehensible. The story of schizophrenia gradually evolved as the culmination of centuries of clinical observation. Morel (1857) first designated this slow, steady deterioration of personality as *démence précoce*. Kraepelin (1896) described the salient features and differentiated the syndrome from organic psychoses. Bleuler (1911) named it schizophrenia to indicate the dissociation of emotional experience and overt behavior. Janet (1924) attributed the behavioral abnormality to childhood difficulties in psychologic adjustment. Kallmann (1952) established the genetic basis of the disease.

The underlying cause of the personality retreat in the multifactorial schizophrenic syndrome is unknown, the clinical ramifications unsettled, the brain pathology obscure. Is it a primary disorder of the brain or a secondary reaction of the brain to a systemic disease? Ignorance of the anatomy and function of the limbic cortex, diencephalon and rhinencephalon, and fallacies of cytochemical methods and of x-ray microspectography mar interpretation of emotional disorders. Nevertheless, there has been a widening of conceptualizations, development of analogizing theories from model psychoses, and synthesis of hallucinogenic drugs despite vicissitudes in methodology. Statistical epidemiological studies fail to confirm the determining role of abnormal early psychologic or sociologic experiences, hence the current shift to neurochemical, neurophysiological, neurometabolic, and neuropharmacological studies of the disordered brain. To be a psychiatrist now-a-days is to inhabit a whole continent of knowledge and to have, perhaps, only a distant acquantance with large areas of those illuminating fields. The long-range research ventures embodied in this lucid thesis are like expeditions to unscaled mountain peaks, with eyes on distant points of revelation and feet fixed on stony realities.

The author adjudges psychiatry by the questions it asks and by the tools it makes available to answer them in unravelling schizophrenia. The biochemical abnormalities may be the cause or consequence of the disease. There is a wider range and lesser reactivity to stimuli than in normal controls; greater stability of the α-rhythm during stress and reduced excitability of the sympathetic-adrenal system; impaired utilization of carbohydrate with elevated blood levels of keto-acids after glucose intake; increased adrenocortical activity; impaired homeostatic control of the circulation indicative of a primary disorder in hypothalamic control. Biochemical relapses precede the clinical by a fortnight, hence the wisdom of understanding schizophrenia as a metabolic disturbance in protein, carbohydrate, and lipid chemistry.

Psychopharmacotherapy is clearing behavior problems more effectively than traditional somatotherapy. The failure of cerebral homeostasis induced by endogenous psychotogens at the synaptic level is combatted by ataractics to establish a lower emotional level of activity without improving the biochemical abnormality. The laws of aberrant behavior yield to the controlled energy of the patient at a liveable level. Chemotherapy is gradually conferring the inalienable right of every individual to the full development of his physical, mental, emotional and social potentialities, and therefore, the inherent right to demand of mankind whatever he needs to supplement his own efforts. Individual problems are always the same but the solutions differ with each era, yet the heart-rending words of Macbeth still appeal today.

> "Canst thou not minister to a mind diseas'd
> Pluck from the memory of rooted sorrow,
> Raze out the written troubles of the brain
> And with some sweet oblivous antidote
> Cleanse the stuff'd bosom of that perilous stuff
> Which weighs upon the heart?"

I. NEWTON KUGELMASS, M.D., Ph.D., Sc.D., *Editor*

ACKNOWLEDGMENTS

I would like to express my gratitude to my teachers in the difficult art of interdisciplinary neuropsychiatric research, and in particular to Dr. Harold E. Himwich, Dr. Hudson Hoagland, Professor Sir Aubrey Lewis and Professor Oliver Zangwill. The future of research in biological psychiatry lies very largely in the creation of interdisciplinary teams of highly trained basic scientists each ideally under the direction of a neuropsychiatrist of a broad scientific and clinical training. Preeminent amongst such teams already existing are of course those at the Galesburg State Research Hospital and the Worcester Foundation for Experimental Biology, together with those at the University of Birmingham under the direction of Dr. P. B. Bradley and at the National Institute of Mental Health and the National Heart Institute of Bethesda, Maryland. These organizations have already made contributions to this field of the utmost value as this review will show.

I am also most grateful to Roche Products Ltd. and in particular to Dr. J. Marks for their manifold aid to our research.

J. R. S.

CONTENTS

SCHIZOPHRENIA

INTRODUCTION

GENERAL PROBLEMS

FOR the last fifty years research workers, in ever increasing numbers, have devoted themselves to the study of the biochemical, pharmacological and physiological aspects of schizophrenia. For many years this work led only to negative, conflicting and in general unsatisfactory and disappointing results. These early workers were handicapped by a number of difficulties that negated their efforts. They lacked, for example, any hypothesis as to what sort of metabolic upset could be associated with schizophrenia and so they had no clue as to what to look for. This entailed in effect that their research programs were determined by whatever analytical techniques were available at the time and which the investigator knew how to apply. These techniques were moreover often crude, inaccurate and misleading. Little enough was known about the normal chemistry of the brain; hence the essential baseline for evaluating abnormality, was in many cases, missing. Then again the problem of providing adequate controls in studies of schizophrenic patients has only recently been taken very seriously. For many years it was considered adequate for the research worker to call at the local psychiatric hospital where he would take samples from a number of patients whom he might never have seen before and whom he would never see again. Only recently, and particularly since the publication of Kety's paper (1959), has the realization taken root that schizophrenic patients differ from normal controls in many ways as well as the specific one of having the disease. If one is carrying out metabolic studies on schizophrenics it is essential to have properly matched controls. This means that the controls must be matched for age, sex, and in particular diet, exercise level and emotional state. In fact the control population should ideally consist of patients with other psychiatric illnesses as well as normal volunteers, living in the metabolic wards with the patients and having exactly the same diet, mouthful by mouthful and cupful by cupful and following the same ward routines. It has been shown that many of the biochemical measures that have been carried out on schizophrenics, and some of which have been claimed to differentiate between schizophrenics and normals, are affected by diet, exercise, posture and emotional state. There is, for instance, the famous investigation where some peculiar phenolic acids found in the urine of schizophrenics were traced by the astute investigators to the fact that the patients had been drinking much more coffee than the controls. The phenolic acids had come from the coffee. Then again many early studies claimed to show abnormalities of carbohydrate metabolism in schizophrenia. However, such factors as exercise, physical fitness, vitamin deficiencies and strong emotions also affect carbohydrate metabolism. Thus the significance of the findings of abnormal types of carbohydrate metabolism in schizophrenia, of the same kind as may be produced by these other agencies, is obscured.

It has been shown (Ashcroft, 1962) that posture and exercise play an important part in determining the composition of the cerebrospinal fluid as obtained by lumbar puncture. The fluid in the ventricles is different in composition from the lumbar fluid and factors which determine to what extent the two fluids are mixed may be of importance in any clinical investigation. Mixing is affected by posture and exercise, which may well differ between patients and controls, as well as by seemingly minor differences in the technique of lumbar puncture.

Thus, in evaluating the results of any research, one must always take into consideration whether the investigator has faithfully controlled all the relevant variables or not. If he has not, one has to estimate to what extent his results are unreliable for this reason. Most of the early work was not adequately controlled and so it will not be reviewed here in detail. The literature is vast, confused and full of conflicting results. Adequate reviews of this work have already been published by Hoskins (1946), Altschule (1953), Richter (1957) and Freeman (1958).

Nor will I be concerned with the detail of the evidence that points to the genetic factors in schizophrenia. It is established that there is a genetic factor in schizophrenia and presumably this must exert its effects through the physiological mechanisms of the body even if these mechanisms are those that subserve the highest psychological functions. This leads us to the question as to whether the disease has a largely pathophysiological or a largely psycho-pathological causation. Again there is no need to waste much time on this sterile argument if we accept three simple principles:

(i) Firstly that the clinical entity now known as "schizophrenia" will probably fall apart into a number of different diseases in much the same way as the "fevers" of eighteenth century medicine be-came differentiated into a number of differing diseases as their causes became known. Diagnosis, in present day psychiatry, except for a few conditions such as general paralysis and phenylketonuria, rests on the uneasy ground of symptomatology. Psychiatric diseases are classified and linked on the basis of the similarily or dissimilarity of their symptoms. This is, of course, necessary at present as we know very little about causes. But when we do presumably other criteria for diagnosis will attain importance, e.g., factors such as disorders of imprinting and conditioning, cybernetic and metabolic disturbances, etc.

(ii) It is also commonly accepted that, in psychiatry, causation is nearly always multiple. A person's genetic endowment interacts through the medium of his nervous system with his life experiences in ways so complex as to render the range of possible reactions large indeed. The environment must be interpreted in terms of the culture into which the individual is born as much as in terms of the conditioning process to which he will continually be subjected as long as he lives. It can hardly be doubted that stress contributes to the development of both neuroses and psychoses. But what *particular* life situations and life experiences are stressful is a matter that is very largely culturally determined.

For example, in our Western culture, people are compelled to be, or pretend to be, practical, aggressive, independent, emotionally secure, self-disciplined, etc. Other cultures demand other qualities (Benedict, 1935). However, many people are born with the genetic endowment that makes them quiet, shy, dependant, insecure, non-aggressive, solitary, etc. A genetic tendency in this direction may be aggravated or alleviated by the particular nature of the person's family, school, sub-culture, etc. In particular in some circumstances the person may be conditioned to feel guilty and ashamed of these personal qualities; in other circumstances guilt and shame may attach to other qualities. In Pueblo culture, for example, the forceful, driving, independent-minded person is likely to become a social outcast and so driven into shame and guilt. Our own culture does not present any well-defined roles for highly introverted, sensitive, shy people. If such people bear the genetic predisposition to schizophrenia and are subjected to unbearable stress, this may precipitate an attack of the illness. The relationship of the "schizoid" personality to schizophrenia is, however, complex. Many schizophrenics had quite unschizoid personalities before the onset of the disease. Many "schizoid" individuals never develop the disease. Nevertheless cultural factors might be expected to play a role in determining the development of schizophrenic illness in a person with a schizoid personality. It would be interesting to see if there was any relation between the "schizoid" personality and schizophrenia in cultures like the Pueblo which attach positive cultural values to some of the personality traits included in this description. The incidence of schizophrenia could be measured together with an estimation of the type of predominant prepsychotic personality in that culture.

The psychological precipitants of a schizophrenic illness may be those situations where a person is made to undergo stress particularly if associated with the ego-weakening emotions of shame, guilt, group-rejection, etc. Childhood experiences of the kind described as important by the Freudian school in the future development of mental illness, may well derive their importance because they constitute those occasions when such emotional reactions were first imprinted on the developing organism. The discoveries of the ethologists have shown how critical experiences at certain ages may have life-long effects. The detail of such imprinting prepares the soil, as it were, for the form of possible future psychiatric disorders. The complex reflex mechanisms governing these ego-damaging emotional reactions are further modulated during the life of the organism by the play of conditioning under circumstances dictated by the culture and by the historical accidents that determine the place of the individual in that culture and his fitness to fill the role. Thus it would be absurd to claim that the answers to the problem of the "cause" of schizophrenia are to be found solely in biochemistry, or in Freudian psychopathology, or learning theory or in any other single discipline. Factors of genetics, metabolism, pathophysiology, conditioning and culture are all relevant.

These considerations do, however, have some bearing on our present subject in that they suggest that the metabolic disorder in schizophrenia may lie in the physiological mechanisms of response to stress and possibly and in particular in the mechanisms that organize the complex ego-damaging emotions of guilt, shame, group-rejection, etc.

(iii) The third general principle whereby one can seek to unify the facts of multiple causation in psychiatry is the positivistic heirarchy of science. Scientists in general subscribe to the belief that all explanations of behavior can eventually be given in physiological terms. The whole Freudian theory could, in principle be reduced to physiological terms. No one has yet done so but this is because we do not yet know enough about the physiology of the brain. But one can easily construct the skeleton of such a reduction using prepositional functions in place of the particular terms that would appear in the definitive reduction. Neurophysiology is, however, progressing very quickly and centers in the brain concerned with pleasure, pain, motivation, goal-seeking, etc. are being described and their functions investigated. Thus the language of a neo-Freudian psychopathology would be expressed in neurophysiological and cybernetic terms to give, along with other relevant explanations of behavior, a common explanation of the full range of behavior in all its full complexity. Terms such as "super-ego," "id," "repression," "censor" could remain as convenient short-hand descriptions or as useful clinical terms, but they would always be capable of reduction to their more basic neurophysiological counterparts which would describe what was actually going on in the relevant brain centers while a painful idea was being repressed, or while dream symbolism was being elaborated and so on.

Thus one must emphasize that, at the present level of our knowledge, biochemical "causes" of schizophrenia (as this term is currently understood), the target of so much current research, are only part causes in many instances of the illness. In some cases, seemingly, the genetic predisposition is so strong that it seems probable that the individual would have developed the illness whatever his life situation. In other cases, such as certain schizophreniform breakdowns in battle or in prisoners undergoing Communist brain washing, the genetic loading may be weak and symptoms only become manifest under the severest stress. In between is a large group where a moderate genetic tendency to develop the disease exists and if certain life stresses are encountered the disease may develop; if they are not the disease may never develop, or it may only develop in old age when the brain is subjected to further assaults in the form of cerebral arteriosclerosis or senile changes.

This preamble enables us to make the working hypothesis that the metabolic or physiological mechanisms at fault in schizophrenia are those which mediate the response to stress and possibly and in particular those stresses that lead to reactions of feelings of group rejection, shame, guilt etc. Rejection or loss of a father or mother figure would appear to be of particular importance in this connection due possibly to the disturbance of imprinting processes that may result. In some cases of schizophrenia the precipitating factors may not be entirely a matter of current psychological stresses directly overloading genetically determined weaknesses of the bodily metabolism. These weak points may themselves be continuously under pressure from faulty imprinting and conditioning and their long term results, or perhaps compensatory mechanisms brought into play by the organism to overcome the ill-effects of these weak points, may themselves be so weakened.

Thus there may be several types of 'biochemical factor' in schizophrenia. **A.** (1) There is the basic fault (or faults) in some metabolic cycle (or cycles) that is (or are) genetically determined; (2) Then there may be compensatory biochemical mechanisms brought into play to try and counter the effect of (1); (3) Then (1) may have secondary, tertiary, etc., effects on other metabolic or physiological mechanisms which may depend for their proper function on the efficient action of (1); (4) The faulty enzyme, or other biochemical agent, may play a part in more than one metabolic cycle and so more than one biochemical system may be disordered from the one fault.

B. (1) In other cases a schizophreniform illness may not be caused by some body-wide metabolic disorder; some genetically determined fault in local brain mechanisms may be involved. The connections from the frontal lobe to the rhinencephalon or hypothalamus, for example, which might be expected to subject instinctual behavior to higher control, may be (biochemically) ill-developed with faulty synapses, neurones, dendrites, axons, or glia. Similarly fronto-temporal connections might be faulty leading to defective control of fantasy and unrealistic thinking. The metabolic disorder would presumably originate in some fault in the template of the DNA which determined the initial construction of the neurones and the manner of their reactions. The localization of the fault may be due to the variety of biochemical specificity that different neurones probably show. Thus, some cases of schizophrenia may be etiologically allied to cerebral palsy. Only the genetically determined damage is more subtle than in classical cerebral palsy and it may be localized to parts of the brain that are only utilized to any great extent when the organism encounters certain types of stress. Thus signs of the damage might only appear in late adolescence and early adulthood when these types of stress become operant; although these factors may have contributed earlier to the development of a "schizoid" personality.

(2) Then, again, a possibility arises from this discussion that the metabolic disorders associated with schizophrenia, or at any rate some of them, may not be uniquely associated with clinical schizophrenia in any qualitative sense. They may occur in a lesser form in the metabolism of schizoid people, or in the metabolism of normal people undergoing complex and painful ego-damaging emotions, or even in the symptom-free relatives of schizophrenics. The chemical distinction between these groups may only be qualitative or regional. In the non-schizophrenics the aberrant metabolic processes may never reach the pitch required to "break bounds" and invade the whole cerebral mechanism of perception, thinking emotional and motor control as they seem to do in schizophrenia.

There may be certain metabolic processes in the visceral brain concerned with the expression and control of certain emotional reactions. These emotional mechanisms might depend on certain chemical reactions, such as N-methylation or metabolic cycles involving adrenochrome, that have only very narrow limits of tolerance for the risk of production of psychotomimetic by-products. Once the limit of tolerance was broken, a run-away reaction might result producing a psychosis by interference with regional and perhaps general cerebral metabolism. A vicious circle would soon build up, for a psychosis is a very stressful state and the faulty mechanisms would be subjected to further overload. The rate of production of these psychotomimetic compounds and the limits of tolerance might be set by genetic factors and by the extent of use and type of habitual reaction of these mechanisms. Thus one might expect to find some metabolic abnormalities in the relatives of schizophrenics. Anastasopoulos and Photiades (1962) report that a large proportion of the relatives of schizophrenic patients react to LSD in a more psychotic manner than do normal controls. In particular, besides the derealization and dreadful panic that may occur in controls, the relatives of schizophrenics are particularly liable to present florid paranoid symptoms. This suggests that their metabolism is different from normals or at least that it becomes so under the influence of LSD.

C. In other cases different genetic factors may be involved that control the development of immune reactions. This may lead to the development of destructive autoimmune reactions (Haddad and Rabe, 1961). An even more remote type of biochemical or physiological explanation of schizophrenia would be that which, I suppose, will one day be attainable, whereby the chemical factors that underlie disorders of imprinting, conditioning, various psychoanalytical mechanisms and the disrupting effects of anxiety, shame, etc., on behavior will be demonstrated both in themselves and how they relate, if they do, to the genetically mediated faults in the biochemistry of the schizophrenic.

In practical terms research on the biochemistry of schizophrenia is at present based on the two main avenues of approach. The target is the postulated main or principle biochemical lesion and this may be sought by two methods: (1) The metabolism of schizophrenic patients may be examined for faults by various ways, and (2) the mode of action of psychotomimetic drugs may be studied at the biochemical and neuropsychopharmacological levels. These two approaches will be dealt with separately in this monograph.

In both two main interconnected difficulties are (i) separating the primary or relevant biochemical disorders from all manner of secondary or irrelevant secondary disorders or side-effects and (ii) of determining whether the fault we find is specific for schizo-phrenia or is common to any state of stress.

Section 2

THE DIRECT STUDY OF SCHIZOPHRENIC METABOLISM

2.1 SPECIFIC HYPOTHESES

THE work carried out before 1950 lacked the benefit of any hypothesis and its course was determined largely by the biochemical techniques that were available at the time. For instance a great deal of work was done on carbohydrate metabolism, because blood glucose is easily measured; on liver function on account of the number of tests of liver function available; on endocrine activity for the same reasons. Furthermore most of this work lacked adequate controls. Its results will be considered where relevant under the particular section concerned.

In 1952, Osmond and Smythies published the first specific biochemical hypothesis of the etiology of schizophrenia. It had been known for over fifty years that the alkaloid mescalin produces a clinical syndrome not dissimilar from that seen in some cases of acute schizophrenia. A great deal of ink has been spilt over the argument whether the mescalin psychosis is like schizophrenia or whether it is merely a toxic psychosis of the type produced by many agents. In particular, people have complained that mescalin produces mainly visual hallucinations which rarely occur in clinical schizophrenia. There are of course some differences between the mescalin psychosis and schizophrenia. However a fair statement of the position might run as follows:

(i) Mescalin causes not only visual hallucinations but also severe anxiety, difficulties in concentration and thinking, flight of ideas (and other types of thought disorder), disorders of affect and depersonalisation very similar to symptoms seen in schizophrenia (Wolbach *et al.*, 1962).

12

(ii) The range of normal reactions to mescalin is very wide between different people and even in one person at different times.

(iii) The effects of mescalin depend to a great extent upon the setting in which it is given. The results will be very different if it is given in a friendly supportive environment or in a cold unfriendly or hostile one. The results obtained by American Indians who use peyote in their ceremonies are different from the results obtained in the case of Westerners who take it without the group setting and belief system of the Indian. In particular the results are different according to the amount of anxiety or fear generated in the individual by the experiment. Anxiety-prone individuals tend to have very unpleasant experiences under mescaline. I, myself, have taken the drug twice at about three months interval. On the first occasion I was startled by the unexpected nature of the changes in perception and experienced a most unpleasant derealisation added to the conviction that this state was permanent. In fact, the state was so unpleasant that I took some sodium succinate as an antidote (Stevenson and Sanchez, 1957). Some twenty minutes afterwards the derealization ended practically instantaneously and I recall darting forward from my chair and seizing someone's foot in token of the sudden return of reality to the world. On the second occasion, in precisely the same environment and with the same dose, a simple and pleasant hallucinosis resulted with no trace of the previous horrors. Presumably I had become accustomed to the remarkable effects of the drug on all streams of psychic activity and furthermore I had had convincing proof of the effectiveness of the antidote. As we will see this correlation between fear and the particular effects of mescaline raises the interesting possibility that some of the more severe psychotomimetic effects of mescalin are mediated by an effect on the sympathetic nervous system, for instance, by interference with the metabolism or action of adrenalin or noradrenalin at certain effector sites; or, of course, the extra load of adrenalin released by fear may interfere with the detoxication of mescalin or may potentiate in some way certain of the activities of mescalin. Thus the clinical effects of mescalin would be greatly altered by the degree of activity in the sympathetic nervous system at the time.

(iv) So, bearing these considerations in mind, we can see how the situational differences between giving mescalin to a normal subject and the onset of an attack of schizophrenia must be responsible to a considerable extent for the differences between the two resulting clinical syndromes. The mescalin taker knows something of what to expect, that it is all an experiment and that his ordeal will be over in a few hours and moreover that effective antidotes are at hand in case the experience becomes too unpleasant. The schizophrenic has no inkling of what to expect, the symptoms last months and not hours, he has little guidance how to cope with them and he is moreover liable to be treated with fear and hostility by his fellows with, one would postulate, a consequent catastrophic effect on the nature and severity of his symptoms. We can see how there would be wide clinical differences between the two conditions even if precisely the same biochemical mechanisms were at fault in each case. In any event the study of the mode of action of mescalin will give us information of the biochemical mechanisms underlying certain types of psychosis. This would allow us to test the performance of these mechanisms in the schizophrenic patient. This research design obviously has many advantages over a blind and purely empirical approach.

Our original hypothesis was based on the fact that the chemical formulae of mescalin and adrenalin are quite similar.

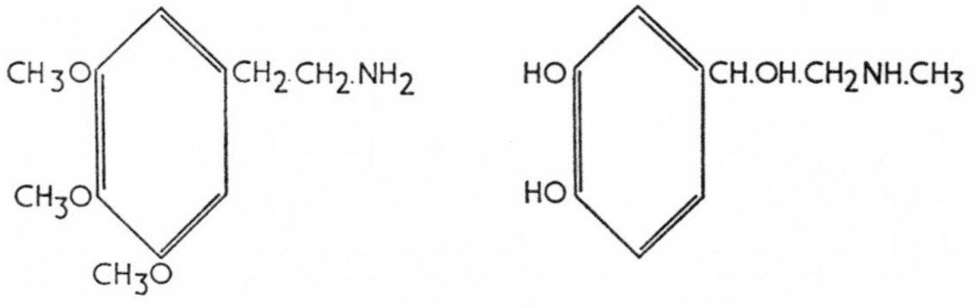

Fig. 1. Structural formulae for mescalin and adrenalin (read figures from left to right and above to below sequentially except where indicated otherwise).

We suggested therefore that schizophrenia might be due in some cases to an abnormality of adrenaline metabolism whereby abnormal metabolites of adrenaline might be produced chemically more like mescalin and with similar psychological properties. This hypothesis satisfied the condition that the metabolic fault in

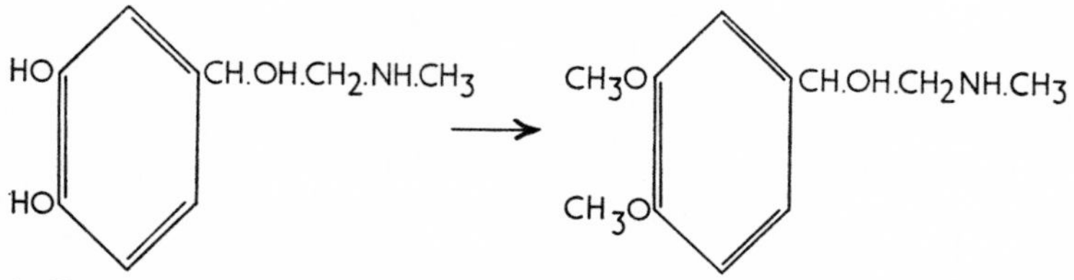

Fig. 2. How adrenalin would be converted by O-methylation into a mescalin-like compound.

schizophrenia should lie in the stress mechanism. The detail was filled in by Harley-Mason (in the same paper) who suggested the biological mechanism by which this might be effected. The hydroxyl groups of adrenalin may be methylated to give methoxy groups and so a mescalin-like structure would result. This constituted the first suggestion in the literature that the metabolism of adrenalin in the human may involve O-methylation. This hypothesis became more interesting when it was demonstrated (Axelrod and Tomchick, 1958; Armstrong *et al.*, 1957) that the main pathway of metabolism of adrenaline is O-methylation in the 3 position to give metanephrine (II in Fig. 3) which in turn is deaminated to give VMA. Then it was shown (Harley-Mason *et al.*, 1958) that a minor metabolite of mescalin in the human is 3-methoxy-4, 5-dihydroxy-phenylethylamine (IV) in Fig. 3. Figure 3 demonstrates how similar this is to the known metabolite of adrenalin.

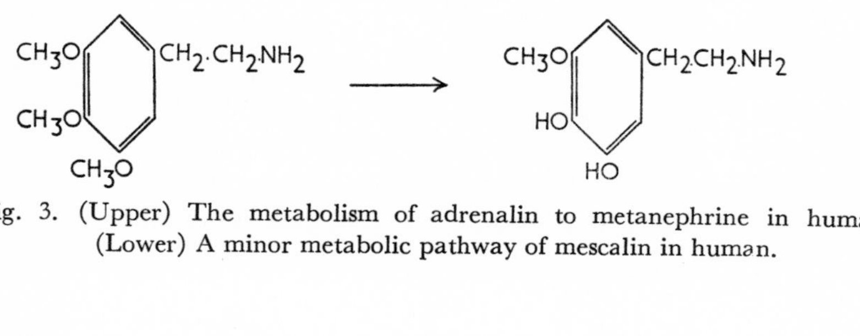

Fig. 3. (Upper) The metabolism of adrenalin to metanephrine in human. (Lower) A minor metabolic pathway of mescalin in human.

Very recently a report has been published by Friedhoff and van Winkle (1962) that they have identified, by using chromatographic methods, 3, 4-dimethoxyphenylethylamine in the urine of 15/19 schizophrenics and 0/14 controls. Medication, but not apparently diet, was controlled. Confirmation of this report is awaited with interest, as the possibility of artifact has not been entirely excluded. Even if this result is confirmed, it cannot be assumed that this compound is the toxic agent responsible for schizophrenia. Smythies and Levy (1960) found that it was only one half as active as mescaline in affecting rat behavior. However, no human studies have as yet been reported. It may, however, represent a wider disorder of methylation. But the metabolism of dopamine, which would appear to be the most likely source of 3, 4-dimethoxyphenylethylamine, has been reported to be normal in schizophrenics (Lenz, 1962). This worker injected the precursor, dopa, and measured the output of 3, 4-dihydroxyphenylacetic acid and homovanillic acid. There were no differences between schizophrenics and five controls.

Thirdly, as we will see later, more direct evidence has recently been obtained (by feeding methionine to schizophrenics) that excess methylation may be directly concerned with schizophrenic symptomatology. Another possibility is that some aberrant pathway of metabolism may develop in schizophrenia such as the production of adrenochrome. There is as yet no positive evidence to support this hypothesis but the theory as a whole has been strengthened by the fact that the earlier report of Hoffer *et al.* (1954) has been confirmed by Grof *et al* (1961) who showed that adrenochrome, in some people, produces 'manifest psychotic reactions' together with marked EEG changes. The drug was given sublingually under double-blind control (using azorubine-S as the placebo) and using a battery of psychological tests. They emphasize the fact that different batches of "adrenochrome" gave differing results—a fact that may have been responsible for the previous confusion on this subject. Adrenochrome is very unstable and it may well be that the actual psychotomimetic agent is some derivative of adrenochrome as von Taubmann and Jantz (1957) have suggested on the basis of their own experimental results.

However, against this hypothesis it must be stated that direct tests of overall adrenaline metabolism in schizophrenia (Resnick *et al.*,1958; Cohen *et al.*, 1959; La Brosse *et al.*, 1961) have revealed no abnormalities either in the relative proportions or amounts of the various known metabolites nor in the rates of utilization of adrenalin or noradrenalin. Nor do schizophrenics react abnormally in any qualitative sense to injected adrenaline (Cardon *et al.*, 1961; Pollin and Goldin, 1961). Nor have any abnormal metabolites of adrenaline been found in schizophrenic blood (Szara *et al.*, 1958; Feldstein, 1959). Of course it is still possible that in schizophrenia there are abnormalities of adrenalin or noradrenalin metabolism localized to the brain. In which case tests of peripheral metabolism would not be relevant particularly as adrenaline crosses the blood-brain barrier in only a very few and localised places. But there is as yet no evidence to show that this is the case.

Furthermore, it is well known that the metabolism of endogenously produced compounds may be quite different from the metabolism of the same compounds when injected.

Costa and Zetler (1959) and Costa (1960) that report there exists a close correlation between hallucinogenic activity of a drug and its capacity to potentiate the action of adrenaline on the denervated nictitating membrane of the cat and on adrenal ascorbic acid depletion in the rat. Thus, sensitivity to adrenalin at effector sites, rather than gross changes of adrenaline metabolism might be of importance in the genesis of psychosis. Walaszek (1960) has claimed that schizophrenic serum given subcutaneously to rabbits four to eight days previously will cause a three to five fold increase in the levels of adrenalin in the hypothalamus as well as some increase in the level of dopamine but no change in serotonin (HT) level. This work has still to be confirmed.

Then, in 1954, Gaddum in Edinburgh and Woolley and Shaw in New York independently suggested that lysergic acid diethylamide (LSD) produces its well-known hallucinogenic effects by an anti-HT action and that a disorder of HT metabolism might be linked with schizophrenia. This hypothesis was based on the fact that LSD has powerful anti-HT action when tested on smooth muscle from various peripheral sources. In its original form this hypothesis is no longer tenable for it has been shown that there is no necessary

connection between peripheral anti-HT action and central psycho-
tometic activity. D-2-brom-lysergic acid diethylamide (BOL)
possesses just as powerful an anti-HT action as LSD yet it is devoid
of psychotomimetic activity. D-1-methyl-2-brom-lysergic acid
diethylamide (MBL 61) has five times the anti-HT action of LSD
but is psychiatrically inert. D-1-methyl lysergic acid diethylamide
(MLA 74) is over eight times as powerful an anti-HT agent as
LSD yet possesses only one-twentieth of its psychotomimetic power.

Furthermore no consistent major abnormalities of HT metabolism have been found in schizophrenics (Feldstein *et al.*, 1958; Kopin,
1959; Rodnight, 1961). Feldstein *et al.* (1958) did find that a few
schizophrenics excrete very large quantities of 5-hydroxindole
acetic acid (5HIAA) and Turner and Mauss (1959) report one
case with a tenfold rise of HT level in the cerebrospinal fluid (most
cases having normal levels). Very recently Jus (1961) carried out
longitudinal studies of single cases and claims to have shown that
cases of acute catatonia have raised levels of blood HT for a day or
so following the onset of the attack. These levels quickly fall to
subnormal levels and only rise to normal following the clinical
recovery of the patient. These findings require confirmation and
their significance evaluation by more extended studies. Brune
and Himwich (1962) have recently reported that urinary tryptamine and indole-3-acetic acid levels do not serve to distinguish
beweeen schizophrenics and controls. But, if each schizophrenic is
followed longitudinally, exacerbations of his psychosis are con-
sistently associated with a rise in the excretion rate for both IAA
and tryptamine; although there are marked differences between
the levels as between different patients.

A third hypothesis has been advanced by McIsaac (1961). This
is based on the close chemical relation between the hallucinogenic
drug harmine and the hormone melatonin. The latter is O-methyl
acetyl serotonin and it can easily be turned into 10-methoxy
harmalan by ring closure and extrusion of water (Fig. 4). This is a
potent HT antagonist and 1 mg. of it completely disrupts the behavior of trained rats. No studies to test its psychotomimetic
properties in humans have apparently as yet been carried out. But
its close relative harmine has been reported to be hallucinogenic
(Pennes and Hoch, 1956).

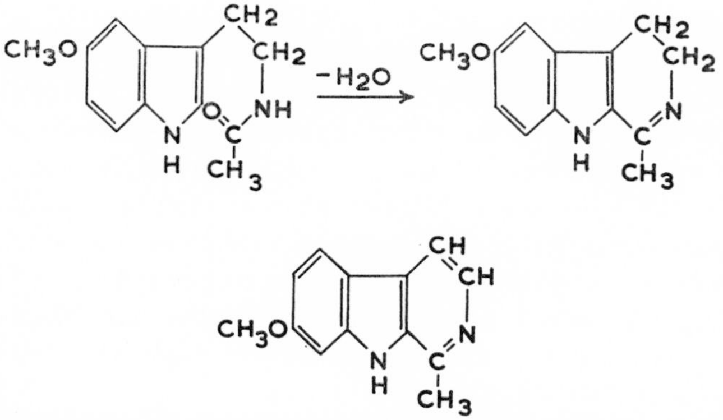

Fig. 4. Melatonin is converted to 10-methoxyharmalan. This is a close relative of harmine (below).

Summary of 2.1.

Research into the biochemical basis of schizophrenia has been aided in recent years by three biochemical theories of etiology. The first, based on the chemical relation between mescalin and adrenalin postulates some disorder of adrenalin metabolism, in particular an excess of methylation. The second, based on the anti-HT affects of LSD, postulates some disorder of the reactions or metabolism of HT. The third, based on the chemical relation between melatonin and harmine, postulates some disorder of melatonin metabolism. Some further developments of the methylation hypothesis will be discussed in Section 3.

2.2 CARBOHYDRATE METABOLISM

In this section I will first summarise the findings of the earlier work on general aspects of carbohydrate metabolism and then discuss some more recent work on intermediate carbohydrate chemistry.

2.2A General Carbohydrate Metabolism

Blood sugar levels are normal in schizophrenia but many reports have appeared stating that glucose tolerance is impaired (see Richter, 1957). Freedman *et al.* (1954) noted that following oral administration of glucose there was a delayed rise to peak values of blood glucose as compared with controls. However there was no difference between the glucose tolerance tests if the glucose was given by the intravenous route. Gildea *et al.* (1943) reported similar results in patients suffering from manic-depressive psychoses. Thus we can conclude that there is a slow absorption of glucose from the gut in psychoses. Henneman *et al.* (1954a) found evidence of a similar disorder of the glucose tolerance curve following oral administration of glucose in cases of multiple sclerosis. Thus, the abnormality is clearly non-specific and furthermore Horwitt *et al.* (1948) were able to produce and correct such changes by controlling the intake of B vitamins.

Henneman *et al.* (1954a) made other measurements of carbohydrate metabolism in psychotic patients and found, following the administration of glucose, an excessive rise in the level of lactic and pyruvic acids in the blood and a greater than normal fall in inorganic phosphate. These changes were also seen in cases of multiple sclerosis (Henneman *et al.*, 1954b). In longitudinal studies some workers report that the metabolic abnormalities approach normality as the clinical condition of the patient improves (Hackfield, 1932; Proctor, Dewar and McNeel, 1944; Henneman *et al.*, 1954a; Meduna, 1950) but Freeman and Zaborenke (1949) reported that in some cases this might happen but in others the patient would show clinical improvement and yet the glucose tolerance remained unchanged or became even more abnormal.

The probable significance of the rise of levels of blood lactic and pyruvic acids in these conditions is suggested by the fact that similar results are obtained when one compares these levels in athletically unfit individuals with trained athletes (Bang, 1936). Hence these findings probably reflect the poor athletic condition of patients with multiple sclerosis and schizophrenia.

Freeman (1946) has shown that both psychotic and neurotic patients in the acute phase are resistant to the hypoglycemic effects of insulin (see also Braceland *et al.*, 1945). Patients with chronic psychoses show a reduced hyperglycemic response to adrenalin. These results may only be secondary to emotional reactions or to the degree of activity of the sympathetic nervous system. However it may be significant that the blood sugar level of people with manic excitement and acute anxiety does not change whereas hyperglycaemia commonly occurs in people profoundly disturbed by fear of catastrophe (Gildea *et al.*, 1935). This correlates with, and may merely reflect, the finding by Weil-Malherbe and Liddell (1954) that plasma adrenalin levels are low in schizophrenia.

2.2B Intermediate Carbohydrate Metabolism

As an introduction to this subject we first review what is known about the metabolism of inorganic phosphate in schizophrenia. Serum inorganic phosphate levels have been reported to be high (Gottfried and Willner, 1947) particularly in catatonia (but not in paranoia; Stevenson *et al.*, 1957). A decreased rate of excretion was noted by Hoagland's group (Hoagland, 1957) in schizophrenics under normal conditions associated with a greater increase than normal in output following the administration of ACTH. Thus it would appear that schizophrenics, and particularly catatonics, show phosphorus retention. Then Örström (1951) found that erythrocytes from normal blood contain approximately 2 mg.% of phosphoglycollic acid whereas those from schizophrenics contain about 4 mg.%. Örström and Skaug (1950) investigated the turnover of adenosine triphosphate (ATP) following the injection of radioactive phosphorus and found that this was slower in chronic schizophrenic patients than in controls. Boszormenyi-Nagy and Gerty (1955) showed that, if normal and schizophrenic blood are incubated with insulin (½ unit per cc. blood), then the schizophrenic blood shows a defective accumulation of energy-rich phosphate in some 80 per cent of the cases. Then, in 1959, Gottlieb, Frohman and their fellow workers at the Lafayette Clinic published the first of their extensive series of papers on the intermediate carbohydrate metabolism in schizophrenia. They first (Gottlieb *et al.*, 1959) established that ATP *levels* in red blood cells both under resting conditions and following the injection of insulin, are normal in schizophrenia. They employed careful controls of physical status and diet. The rate of turn over of ATP, however, was higher in chronic schizophrenics than in either normal controls or acute schizophrenics. Thus their results differ from those of Örström and Skaug, but they were able to confirm Boszoremenyi-Nagy and Gerty's finding that schizophrenics red blood cells are unable to mobilize energy rich phosphate following, in these experiments, the injection of insulin. The specific activity of ATP rose threefold in the control group, doubled in the acute schizophrenic group but it fell markedly in the chronic schizophrenic group. It should be noted that "chronic" in this instance refers to the fact that the patients show Bleuler's "primary symptoms" of schizophrenia rather than to the length of time that the illness has lasted. This and possible different levels of stress in their patients may explain the differences between their findings and those of Örström and Skaug. They obtained the same results on measuring ADP levels and rates of turn over. In the case of fructose 1.6. diphosphate, however, both the schizophrenic groups had higher levels of turnover than the control group, and following the injection of insulin, the specific activity of the control group showed a fourfold rise and the specific activities of both schizophrenic groups fell.

They bring forward two hypotheses to explain their finding of a higher rate of ATP turnover in the chronic schizophrenic group under resting conditions (i) that this truely represents a raised turnover of ATP or (ii) that it is due to the depression of the re-action: $2ADP \rightarrow ATP + AMP$ (catalysed by myokinase) in schizo-phrenics. ATP formed in this manner would incorporate no radio-active phosphorus and thus it would dilute the radioactive ATP formed by the ordinary pathway and so give a false appearance of lower total turnover in the controls. This interpretation correlates with a suggestion made recently by Takahashi and Akabane (1960). They found that brain hexokinase activity is reduced both in schizophrenic patients and in rats to whom methamphetamine had been administered for a long time. They suggest that this effect is brought about as follows. The primary fault in each instance is inhibition of myokinase activity (which catalyses the reaction $2ADP \rightarrow ATP + AMP$). This would lead to an accumulation of ADP and this is an inhibitor of hexokinase. Against this however is the fact that the Lafayette group found no change in the level of ADP in schizophrenic red blood cells. These hypotheses remain purely speculative as no further work seems to have been carried out to test any of them.

The amount of glucose metabolised by red blood cells via the Meyerhof scheme of anaerobic glycolosis (with the production of pyruvate, lactate and ATP) was then compared (Frohman *et al.*, 1960a) with the amount metabolised via the hexosemonophosphate shunt to ribose-1-phosphate (which is used in the synthesis of nucleo-proteins and the components of many enzyme systems). The method which they claim does this measures the evolution of radio-active CO_2 from glucose labelled in the 1 position and from glucose labeled in the 6-position. Glucose metabolized by the Meyerhof scheme yields CO_2 from both the 1 and the 6 carbons whereas that metabolised via the ribose pathway yields CO_2 from the 1 carbon only.

Their results appeared to show that controls, following the injection of insulin, increased the amount of glucose metabolised by the Meyerhof pathway of energy production in proportion to the amount passing down the ribose synthetic pathway. This increase can account for the increased rate of ATP turnover the group had previously reported under these conditions. In the case of schizophrenics no change in this ratio was noted. This was held to be consistent with the inability of schizophrenic red blood cells to increase their rate of turnover of ATP under these conditions. Human blood cells having no nuclei lack the Krebs cycle: hence the energy needed for the reaction ADP→ATP comes largely from the Meyerhof scheme of glycolysis.

However, these conclusions must be modified on the following grounds. As Wood (1955) states there are many intermediate steps in metabolism before the labelled carbon atoms are actually given off as CO_2. Many of these intermediate compounds are fully interconvertible with fatty or amino acids. Hence the amount of radioactive CO_2 given off depends as much on the patency of these leaks whereby radioactive carbon atoms can be diverted to protein and fat (in the Meyerhof scheme) and hence in part avoid conversion to CO_2. The existence of these leaks is suggested by the fact that their control subjects appear from their tables to pass twenty-three times as much glucose down the ribose pathway as they do down the Meyerhof pathway (Frohman *et al.*, 1960a) whereas it is known, at least in the case of the liver, that only 75 per cent of glucose metabolised to CO_2 goes down the ribose pathway (Bloom *et al.*, 1953).

Thus, we must modify their conclusions as follows. Their results suggest that red cells from schizophrenic patients, without insulin, either pass a greater proportion of glucose down the Meyerhof pathway than is the case in normals, or some of the leaks away to protein and fat metabolism on this pathway may be closed off. Similarly, following the injection of insulin, the schizophrenic red cells may not be able to pass more glucose down this energy pathway (as can the normal) or they may not be able to close off these leaks any further which normal red cell metabolism may be able to do. Or, of course these two effects may both operate.

Frohman *et al.* (1960b) then measured the amount of lactic acid and pyruvic acid produced by chicken red cells (nucleated) incubated in normal and in schizophrenic plasma. In the latter the lactate level was 23 per cent higher and the pyruvate level 30 percent lower than in normals. The lactate/pyruvate ratio was raised 77 per cent. They suggested that this implied that there was some inhibitor of aerobic metabolism in schizophrenic plasma. This rise in the lactate/pyruvate ratio can be correlated with the inability of the schizophrenic to switch to the Meyerhof scheme of glucose metabolism under insulin as follows. The ribose pathway depends on TPN whereas the Meyerhof scheme uses DPN. Any fault in the H transport mechanism whereby DPN is normally reconstituted from $DPNH_2$ would impair the Meyerhof scheme and would bring into play compensatory mechanisms for the reconstitution of DPN, namely:

$$DPNH_2 \diagdown \quad \diagup PYRUVATE$$
$$DPN \diagup \quad \diagdown LACTATE$$

This would lead to the accumulation of lactate and the rise in the lactate/pyruvate ratio actually observed.

Frohman *et al.* (1960c) determined by fractionation methods that the active agent responsible for these changes is located in the α-globulin fraction. It is thermolabile and stable between pH 6 and 9. In their latest work (Frohman, 1962) they confirmed that these changes are only seen in schizophrenia and not in any of the other diseases that they tested. In particular they were not seen in cases of childhood schizophrenia. This was so even in those cases that had grown to adulthood. Their plasma behaved like normal plasma and showed no signs of the reactions characteristic of "chronic" schizophrenia. This suggests that childhood schizophrenia and adult schizophrenia are two different diseases.

Very recently they have shown that for the L/P ratio, the factor is present in adult schizophrenia only after a certain amount of exercise (Latham *et al.*, 1962). The parameter used was the lactate/pyruvate ratio produced by chicken erythrocytes in plasma from schizophrenic subjects. This renders interpretations of their results somewhat difficult. This finding suggests that the metabolic fault they have detected cannot be directly concerned in the genesis of schizophrenia and their "factor" is not the specific causal agent of the disease—otherwise exercise should make schizophrenics worse, which it does not. Neither would it appear that one can simply account for these results on a basis of the lack of physical fitness of most schizophrenic patients, although a control study of long term chronic patients with other diseases confined to bed for years, as well as studies of athletes, might throw some light on this. One could suggest that the primary fault in schizophrenia, say of methylation processes, disturbs muscle or liver metabolism in such a way that the metabolic response to exercise is altered and the Frohman serum "factor" is produced, which itself has only secondary effects. Of course one could speculate that the Frohman "factor" produced, or at least released into the blood stream by exercise, is a cerebral toxin. Hence the immobility of catatonic patients is a biological defence reaction. On the other hand it may not really be important whether the Frohman factor is or is not present in the plasma. It may be present in schizophrenic tissues, including the brain, at all times and levels in the plasma may not be important etiologically as the factor may not be able to cross the blood-brain barrier. By this interpretation the total schizophrenic metabolism produces the Frohman factor and the brain levels of this determine the course of the disease. Raised plasma levels following exercise is a useful index, as plasma is easily obtained, but not essential. This hypothesis could be tested by seeing if biopsy specimens of schizophrenic organs (especially brain obtained at leucotomy) contain the Frohman factor. This might suggest that they are not dealing with the basic metabolic fault—as increased exercise levels do not as far as I know lead to deterioration of schizophrenic patients— but with some secondary phenomenon.

The bulk of this work remains to be confirmed by other workers and steps should be taken to exclude the possibility that the toxic agent is not merely 6-sulphatoxyskatole or other bacterial degradation products of aminoacids derived from gut bacteria that have been demonstrated in excess in mentally ill people (Rodnight, 1961).

2.2C Further Studies of Carbohydrate Metabolism

Plasma from four out of nine schizophrenics inhibited the uptake of glucose by rat diaphragm (Haavaldsen *et al.*, 1958). These same patients also showed a pathological insulin tolerance curve and in some ketonuria was found. The diet was not, however, controlled. Streifler and Kornbluth (1959) claimed to have found a similar effect using rat retina. Holmberg *et al.* (1960) measured the rate of uptake of C14 glucose in the brains of mice. They found that normal human serum contains a factor that inhibits this rate of uptake and that this effect was more marked in the case of schizophrenic serum but not to a statistically significant extent. Patients in mental hospitals with diseases other than schizophrenia gave intermediate values. In this series diet and medication were well controlled. They found one additional feature of interest. In the schizophrenic group, but no other, the degree of inhibition of glucose uptake increased with age ($p < 0.001$). They suggested that this might be due to a cumulative effect of the schizophrenic process.

Moya *et. al* (1958) injected extracts from schizophrenic urine into rabbits and found that they induced a significantly greater degree of hyperglycaemia than did such extracts from the urine of normal controls. Moreover the hyperglycaemia reached its maximum level three hours after the injection as compared with one hour in the controls. The extracts were also much more toxic to the rabbits. Diagnosis and medication were controlled but they make no mention of any dietary control. However this same effect had already been reported by Meduna and Vaichulis (1948) and Morgan and Pilgrim (1952).

Sacks (1959), using a complex method of measuring cerebral metabolism in human subjects based on the administration of glucose labelled with C14 in different positions in the molecule, found that psychotic patients evolve less CO_2 from glucose than do normal controls. They utilize one-third less glucose and there is a greater than normal dilution of glucose intermediates by intermediate metabolites from protein and/or fat metabolism. This fact emphasizes the importance of the "leaks" between the Meyerhof scheme of glucose metabolism and protein and fat metabolism to which I drew attention when discussing the work of the Lafayette Clinic. In the latter case the leaks were in the opposite direction. However, the interchange of metabolites is a dynamic two-way process and these results point the need for control of this factor by the Lafayette Clinic group, particularly so as further work by Sacks suggests that pyruvate is the metabolic level at which the dilution he noted takes place.

Arnold and Hofmann (1962)* have very recently reported a study of levels and specific activity of ATP, ADP, AMP, and fructose—1, 6—diphosphate in normals and schizophrenics before and after an intravenous injection of succinic acid. They found no differences in resting intermediate carbohydrate metabolism between the two groups (in contrast to Frohman's findings) but following the administration of succinic acid there was a striking difference. In normals, this significantly increased the specific activity and P^{32} uptake of ATP, whereas schizophrenics did not show this reaction. Moreover, the symptom-free relatives of schizophrenics showed a more sluggish P^{32} uptake with ATP than normal. Thus, these workers confirm a disturbance of carbohydrate metabolism which they locate below the phosphoglyceric aldehyddehydrogenase stage which is manifest only when "stress" (i.e., succinic acid injection) is applied. Therefore, the important features of the Lafayette Clinic's findings have been confirmed.

Summary 2.2

The positive findings that have been reported in the field of disordered carbohydrate metabolism in schizophrenia may be summarized as follows:

(1) Schizophrenic plasma contains a factor that (i) increases the rate of turnover of ATP and ADP in red blood cells and/or inhibits the reaction $2ADP \rightarrow ATP + AMP$. It also renders this rate of turnover incapable of being increased by the action of insulin; (ii)

---

*Arnold, O. H. and Hofmann, G.: Der intermediäre Phosphatstoffwechsel des Erythrozyren bei Normalpersonen, Schizophreninen und deren Familien-angehörigen unter Bernsteinsäuvebelastung. *Weiner Z. f. Nervenheilkunde u. Grenzgebiete, 19*:15,1962.

it either causes an increase in the proportion of glucose passing down the Meyerhof scheme as compared with the amount passing down the ribose pathway (which proportion cannot however be increased by insulin as it can in normals) and/or it closes off the leaks from the Meyerhof scheme into protein and/or fat metabolism (which leaks may not be able to be further closed off by the action of insulin); (iii) it causes, following some exercise on part of the patient, an elevation of the lactate/pyruvate ratio suggesting some inhibition of aerobic metabolism. This factor was localised to the α-globulin fraction of serum. Similar findings have been reported following the injection of succinate.

(2) Another factor (also in the α-globulin fraction) has been described by other workers which may inhibit the uptake of glucose by rat diaphragm and retina.

(3) Another factor causes hyperglycaemia when injected into rabbits.

(4) A factor decreases the amount of glucose oxidized by the brain with dilution at, possibly, the pyruvate level, by intermediates from lipid and/or protein metabolism.

These different results seem to make up some kind of coherent account and of course some of these separate factors may turn out to be the same.

2.3 THE TOXICITY OF SCHIZOPHRENIC BODY FLUIDS

Bergen *et al.* (1960b), using quantitative methods of evaluation, have confirmed previous reports (Winter and Flataker, 1958) that plasma from schizophrenic patients is significantly more toxic to rats and mice—in the sense of disruption of learned behavior patterns—than is plasma from normal controls. Moreover, they have shown that the toxic factor will diffuse across a semipermeable membrane, if a carrier protein is provided on the further side. The factor must therefore be a small molecule attached to the protein. Using fractionation methods the maximum toxic effect was localised to the globulin fraction. Very recently this group (Bergen *et al.*, 1961) extended this work using a method devised by Smythies *et al.* (1960) which tests the effect of drugs on the potential evoked in the optic cortex of unanesthetized rabbits by a light flash in the eye. Psychotomimetic drugs such as mescalin and LSD induce a potentiation of these potentials at low dosage and an inhibition at high doses. Globulin fractions from schizophrenic sera produce a significantly greater degree of inhibition of the evoked potential than did sera from normal individuals. German (1961) has tested the effect of placing schizophrenic serum topically on rat cortex and recording the potential evoked in somatosensory cortex by peripheral stimulation. This results in an increase in the amplitude of the negative component of the response by a mean factor of 2.3 fold (S.D. 0.56; range 1.67-3.52). Normal serum applied in an identical fashion produced an increase of only 1.27 fold (S.D. 0.1; range 1.13-1.47) Medication and diagnosis were controlled but not apparently diet. The significance of these results will be discussed in Section 3.

Geiger (1960) has examined the influence of schizophrenic serum on neurones grown in tissue culture. Serum was obtained from acute schizophrenics, not under any drug treatment but with no apparent control of diet. The following were amongst the effects noted: (i) glial motility was enhanced (an effect similar to that induced by HT); (ii) the neural cytoplasm showed increased pulsatile and pumping movements particularly in the case of cells from the temporal lobe and the boutons showed an increase in density; (iii) fine undulating membranes appeared on cell surfaces as well as on axons and dendrites and the transfer of material from oligodendroglia to neurones became more evident; and (iv) after some three days the dendrites showed a tendency to flatten out and to retract and the liponucleoprotein granules shrank and became more diffuse (an effect similar to that obtained with LSD) and they might disappear. Serum from hundreds of normal individuals never induced these changes. Interestingly enough if a Tyrode extract of normal brain was added together with the schizophrenic serum, the toxic effects of the latter were prevented.

Wada and Gibson (1959) have prepared extracts from schizophrenic and from normal urine and they injected these into the cisterna or lateral ventricles of cats and monkeys. The medication, but not the diet, was controlled. The schizophrenic extracts produced varieties of aberrant behavioral responses, e.g., rage states and a loss of the affectionate response together with recurrent stuporose and catatonic states in about half the animals. These effects, except for one brief period of stupor in one monkey, were not seen following the injection of the extracts from normal urine. Furthermore the normal extracts did not produce any changes in the EEG whereas the schizophrenic extracts frequently produced abnormal slow waves, sharp waves and spikes.

Bishop (1960) has contributed some observations on the effect of schizophrenic and normal plasma on instrumental conditioned behavior in rats. The patients were all chronic schizophrenics and were well controlled for diagnosis, diet, exercise, medication and absence of organic illness. Most of the trials were run blind. He found that animals injected with schizophrenic plasma showed a significant impairment ($p < 0.01$) of new learning but no impairment of the retention of overlearning. Both normal and schizophrenic plasma have an irritant effect on the rat peritoneum making the rats sluggish and ataxic. This tends to make them stay in their cages and inhibits the normal exploratory drive. The effect can be overcome by conditioned stimuli associated with some painful experience. Only under these conditions does the more toxic effect of the schizophrenic plasma become manifest.

Walaszek (1960) has recently reviewed the effect of schizophrenic serum on the CEPR ("cortical epinephrine pressor response"). If adrenaline is applied locally to the cerebral cortex of the rabbit a rise in blood pressure is normally evoked. If, at the same time, normal serum is injected subcutaneously into the rabbit, the usual response is obtained in 85 per cent of the cases and a diminished response in 15 per cent (total of 45 experiments). If, however, schizophrenic serum is injected, a normal response is obtained in only 26.5 per cent of cases, a diminished response in 16 per cent, no response in 31 per cent and a reversed response (e.g., a fall in blood pressure) in 26.5 per cent of cases (total of 68 experiments). In these cases the response to adrenaline injected intravenously was unchanged; thus any peripheral site of action can be ruled out. In the schizophrenic cases the levels of adrenalin and dopamine in the hypothalamus were raised. This interesting work awaits confirmation. Lastly Bercel (1959), using Witt's technique, has shown that serum from cases of catatonic schizophrenia causes spiders to spin abnormal webs whereas serum from paranoid schizophrenics and from depressed patients has no effect.

Summary 2.3

The earlier work suggesting that schizophrenic body fluids were more toxic to a number of biological test systems (see Smythies, 1960) has been confirmed and extended using more rigorous controls and better quantitative tests and statistical design. This more recent work has shown that schizophrenic serum or plasma produces (i) abnormalities in neurones and glia grown in tissue culture and in the electrical responses of neurones; (ii) impairment in new learning in the rat; (iii) an inhibition or reversal of the CEPR and (iv) abnormalities in the web spinning behavior of spiders. Extracts from schizophrenic urine produced behavioral and EEG changes when injected intrathecally in monkeys and cats.

However it must be said that there is as yet no certain evidence that this toxicity is specific for schizophrenia and some measures (Bergen *et al.*, 1960b) suggest that it may occur in other disease states. Furthermore a number of toxins may be involved (a) a postulated specific schizophrenic toxin, (b) bacterial degradation products of tryptophane from the gut (c) a toxic effect may be due to some qualitative imbalance of normal plasma constituents produced by any severe state of stress, or (d) a secondary effect due to some abnormal byproduct of muscular activity in schizophrenics. Most of the present work in this field needs repeating to disentangle this confusion by using proper controls, e.g., with sterilized gut, with control of amount of exercise, with other psychiatric patients and people with various emotional disturbances as well as the usual "normal" controls.

2.4 OTHER METABOLIC ABNORMALITIES

The next section will deal with some recent reports of disordered metabolism of various compounds or classes of compounds in schizophrenia.

2.4A Neuraminic Acid

Bogoch and his group have investigated the levels of neuraminic (sialic acid) and related compounds in the cerebrospinal fluid of schizophrenic patients with dietary and double blind control. They found in a series of 700 patients (Bogoch *et al.*, 1959) that the levels

were abnormally low. A level of 41 γ/cc. gave a useful division
between schizophrenics and normal controls with some 10 per cent
overlap. Christoni and Zappoli (1960) have confirmed this result.
In a more recent investigation Bogoch *et al.* (1960) measured the
levels of hexoseamine (as galactoseamine) and neuraminic acid
in a number of conditions. They report significantly low values of
hexoseamine in a number of conditions including schizophrenia,
manic-depressive psychosis and organic brain damage. These
levels tended to return to normal in each case when clinical improvement took place. Frohman *et al.* (1960c) found, however,
two and one-half times *as much* neuraminic acid in their active
fraction from schizophrenic plasma as from normal plasma.
Methods for measuring neuraminic acid are not yet well established
and this work requires further confirmation. In this connection
it is of interest to note that the influenza virus has a specific action
on the sialic acid end-groups of mucoproteins. The virus acts as a
true enzyme and gives rise to the release of N-acetyl neuraminic
acid (Axelrod, 1960). The not uncommon occurrence of severe
depressions after influenza may be connected with this effect.

2.4B Indoles in Schizophrenia

Reports have appeared in the literature from time to time claim-
ing either higher levels of normal indoles (such as 5HIAA) or
aberrant indoles (such as bufotenin or spots of various colors on
chromatograms). However nothing can be regarded as established
in this field except as noted in Section 2. Rodnight has shown
(Rodnight and Aves, 1958) that some mentally ill patients, particularly depressives, excrete an excess of 6-sulphatoxy skatole in
their urine. However this falls to very low levels if the gut is sterilized by feeding antibiotics and no change results in the clinical
condition. Other bacterial degradation products of tryptophane
are sometimes found (e.g., IAA, indol carboxylic acid conjugates
and indoxyl glucuronide). Commenting on his failure to detect
any abnormal indole in schizophrenic blood, Rodnight, in a recent
comprehensive review (1961) of the subject, points out that the
present methods of detection have a threshold of about 0.5 γ/cc.
blood and some indoles (notably LSD) are active in a blood concentration of 0.02γ/cc So it remains possible that more sensitive

analytical methods may discover some abnormal indoles in schizophrenic body fluids. The metabolic abnormality may also be confined to nervous tissue.

2.4C Tryptophane Metabolism

Encouraging progress has recently been made in this field for some experimental work has actually been confirmed by other workers, an event that has been somewhat rare in schizophrenia research to date. Price *et al.* (1959) reported that six out of a total of nineteen schizophrenics metabolished l-tryptophane abnormally. Following a loading dose of tryptophane they excreted excessive amounts of kynurenic acid, o-aminohippuric acid, acetylkynurenine and hydroxykynurenine and they excreted lesser amounts of N-methyl-2-pyridone-carboxamide (NMPC) when compared with normal controls. Similar changes were also found in cases of porphyria and other psychoses. Tryptophane was metabolised normally by patients with purely neurological disorders. The type of abnormality suggested some deficiency of pyridoxine but no chemical nor clinical improvement followed administration of this compound. Brown *et al.* (1960) were not able to confirm most of these results in nine cases. Patients, without tryptophane loading did excrete less NMPC but diet was not controlled. However, Benassi *et al.* (1961) were able to confirm many of Price's findings.

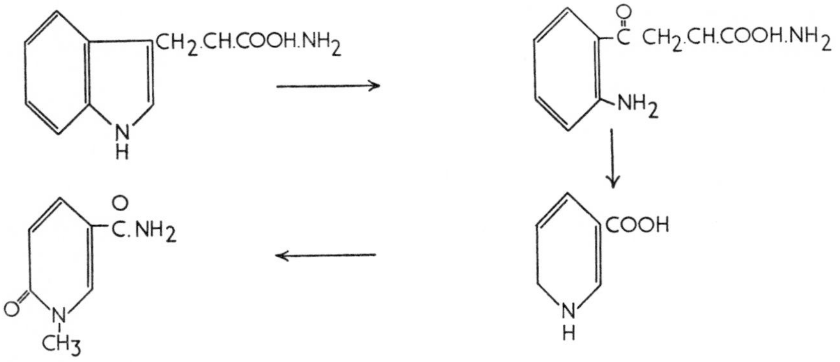

Fig. 5. Part of the kynurenine pathway of tryptophan metabolism: tryptophan to kynurenine to nicotinic acid to MPCA.

They reported an excessive excretion of kynurenine and its relations in schizophrenia and a lessened excretion of NMPC. Their
experiments were well controlled for age, sex, motility, weight and
diet. The lowered values of NMPC excretion gain in interest because its precursor is N-methyl nicotinamide. Van Tamelan (1953)
has speculated that N-methyl nicotinamide could combine with
the p-quinoneimine form of 5-HTP or 5-HIAA to give rise to an
LSD-like structure.

2.4D Aminoacids

A most interesting and significant finding by Kety's group (Pollin
et al., 1961) has been that feeding large doses of individual aminoacids to schizophrenics maintained on iproniazid affected their
clinical state. L-tryptophane produced, in five out of seven cases,
an elevation of mood amounting at times to euphoria, extraverted
and uninhibited behavior and increased deep tendon reflexes. It
produced much the same effects however in normal people. When
the tryptophane was suddenly stopped "withdrawal" symptoms
in the form of hostility and depression resulted. Of more interest
was the fact that l-methionine produced in four out of nine patients, an exacerbation of their schizophrenic symptoms, e.g., an
increase in thought disorder reaching at times word salad proportions, increased anxiety often amounting to panic and increased
motor activity, depression and hallucinations. As methionine is a
donor of methyl groups this lends support to our original hypothesis (Osmond and Smythies, 1952) that an excess of methylation is
linked with the genesis of the disorder. It would be of interest to see
if another methyl donor such as serine, had similar effects and if
feeding a methyl acceptor such as glycocyamine along with the
methionine nullified the effects of the latter. Himwich and Brune
(1963) have recently confirmed these findings (under MAOI cover)
with methionine and moreover, they have shown that another
methyl donor—betaine—produces rather similar results. They distinguish between two behavioral reactions characteristic of these
agents. The first is a cluster of symptoms like those seen in alcoholic
intoxication (i.e., euphoria, sleepiness and confusion) whereas, the
second is an accentuation of the schizophrenic symptoms themselves (e.g., an exacerbation of hallucinations and delusions and an

increase in the disorganization of thought). The authors warn that no simple casual linkage between excess methylation and the etiology of the natural psychoses can be deduced from their findings because the symptoms of alcoholic intoxication do not occur in the natural psychoses. However, this intoxication may be produced by properties of these agents other than their action as methyl donors—properties that they may share for instance with tryptophane which also induces this state of intoxication (although many other amino acids do not) without exacerbating the schizophrenic sysptoms (Pollin *et al.*, 1961).

2.4E Histamine

Recently some more work has been done on the role of histamine in schizophrenia. Lucy (1954) demonstrated that schizophrenics react clinically less to injected histamine and Weckowicz and Hall (1958) showed that they react with smaller wheals following injection of histamine into their skins. The histaminolytic activity of schizophrenic serum is higher than normal (Bernstein *et al.*, 1960) due to a higher histamine content of the serum. However, the histaminase content goes very much higher in pregnancy. The skin of schizophrenics contains fewer mast cells than normal (Le Blanc, 1961). This worker also confirmed that their cutaneous response to injected histamine is much smaller than normal. As the patients improved so did their skin response. If they did not improve it did not do so. This effect has also been confirmed by Simpson and Kline (1961).

2.5 IMMUNITY AND ALLIED REACTIONS

Recently thought has been directed towards the possibility that schizophrenia may be associated with an autoimmune reaction. Haddad and Rabe (1961) have demonstrated striking differences between the immunological properties of schizophrenic and normal sera. Guinea pigs were sensitized with pooled sera from chronic schizophrenics. After three weeks they were desensitized with serum from normal controls. The animals were then repeatedly challenged with normal serum until they gave no further anaphylactic reactions. They were then challenged with pooled schizophrenic serum and showed anaphylactic reactions in every case.

These reactions were also obtained by using non-pooled sera from individual patients. Thus the various schizophrenic patients had one or more antigens in common that were not present in the normal sera that had been used for desensitization.

Fessel (1961) showed that psychotic patients have an excessive incidence of rheumatoid factor and lupus factor in their sera. Fessel and Grunbaum (1961) examined the sera of 162 patients with chronic psychosis by electrophoretic methods. 84 of these specimens of sera contained the rheumatic factor (F II positive); forty-six contained neither the rheumatoid nor the lupus factor (F II negative). As controls fifty long-term prisoners in Alcatraz Federal Penitentiary were used. None of their sera contained lupus or rheumatoid factor. The major qualitative abnormalities in the schizophrenic group were as follows: (i) an abnormally shaped gamma globulin curve in 32 per cent; (ii) a sharp line super-imposed on the gamma globulin in 17 per cent; splitting of the alpha$_2$ globulin in 10 per cent. The main quantitative abnormalities were an increase in gamma globulins in all patients and a significant elevation of s 19 macroglobulins in some. They point out that simple malnutrition does not cause such abnormalities nor does prolonged immobility. But in some cases they could not exclude the possible effects of previous treatment, e.g., insulin antibodies derived from previous insulin shock treatment. They excluded liver disease as the serum transminase levels were normal in nearly all patients.

It is interesting to speculate what relationship these findings bear to the location of the toxic factor in schizophrenic serum (as tested on rat behavior) by Bergen *et al.* (1960b) to the globulin fraction and the location in this same fraction by the group at the Lafayette Clinic of the factor in schizophrenic serum responsible for disturbing intermediate carbohydrate metabolism.

Recently Goodman *et al.* (1961) report increased amounts of orosomucoid (a glycoprotein) in schizophrenic plasma as well as in many organic diseases including rheumatoid arthritis. Chronic schizophrenics show a slower rise than normal controls in antibody formation following the administration of tularemia and staphylococal vaccines (Kerbikov, 1961) The antibody response can be stimulated by some methods of therapy.

Summaries 2.4 and 2.5

In these sections a number of miscellaneous abnormalities of metabolism and immune reaction have been reported. Disorders of the levels of neuraminic acid and related compounds in the cerebrospinal fluid of cases suffering from a variety of diseases await confirmation. The work previously described under the heading of indoles has now developed to such an extent as to make it necessary to specify to which class of indoles we are referring. Abnormalities of tryptophane metabolism have been found and confirmed. However, the same changes were found in porphyria and other psychoses (although not in purely neurological disorders). A significant finding has been that feeding large doses of methionine to schizophrenic patients makes their symptoms much worse. This suggests some relation between the disease and excess methylation. Recent work on the role of histamine in schizophrenia has abundantly confirmed the fact that schizophrenics show a lesser clinical and physiological response to histamine. This appears to be related to the fact that they have higher serum histaminase levels than normal. This links up with the finding of disorders of the immunological reaction in schizophrenics that have been demonstrated in three different ways. Disorders in the composition of the plasma proteins have been shown by electrophoretic methods.

DISCUSSION OF SECTION 2

It will be clear from this review that research in this field has entered upon an active state of growth. Researchers are pursuing some very promising leads which apparently diverge at present but may well converge again later. The variety of primary, secondary and tertiary specific biochemical abnormalities to be expected in schizophrenia and the various non-specific reactions outlined in Section 1 will be recalled. Some of these leads may be following the same abnormality only at different levels of its manifestation.

There is now good evidence that various bodily constituents, in particular HT, tryptamine, melatonin and adrenaline are closely allied chemically to potent psychtomimetic drugs (DMT, DET, psilocybin, harmine, adrenochrome). An enzyme capable of chang-

ing such normal bodily constituents into these drugs has actually
been isolated from mammalian tissues (see Section 3.5) and testing
the effect of overloading this system in schizophrenics (by feeding
methionine) actually aggravates their symptoms. Thus experimental results that offer some support to one or other of the three
specific hypotheses of the etiology of the illness are already coming
to hand.

An interrelated complex of disorders of carbohydrate and phosphate metabolism have been reported in schizophrenia. Schizophrenics in general appear to retain inorganic phosphate. Most of
the work on the intermediate carbohydrate metabolism of schizophrenics has been carried out at Lafayette Clinic in Detroit. With
certain modifications their general conclusions seem to follow from
their experimental findings although they have left a number of
loose ends to be tidied up, for instance: the real significance of the
apparently raised rate of turnover of ATP in chronic schizophrenia
and which of the two hypotheses they bring forward to account for
this is correct and why their results do not correspond at all points
with those of Örström and Skaug. Lastly, their work needs repeating on schizophrenics after they have been fed antibiotics to
sterilize the gut and the recently discovered role of exercise needs
explanation.

Work is also actively proceeding to localize and identify the toxic
factor in schizophrenic serum, the existence of which has by now
been abundantly demonstrated by a great variety of tests. Many
workers agree in localizing this factor in the globulin fraction of the
serum. This links up in interesting ways with the disorders of immunological responses that have been reported in schizophrenia.
Clearly, some common factor may be involved.

THE MODEL PSYCHOSES

3.1 INTRODUCTION

THE relationship between the mescalin psychosis and clinical schizophrenia was discussed in section 2. Whatever this relationship may eventually turn out to be, it can hardly be denied that the model psychoses have proven extremely useful in our studies of psychosis. They have enabled us to make a wider range of enquiries into human reactions than would have been possible otherwise and, of course, they have enabled us to make far more extensive biochemical, pharmacological and neurophysiological studies in animals. If we knew the precise chemical mechanisms by which these agents of known chemical structure produce their effects then at least we would know the biochemical mechanisms underlying some forms of psychosis. The performance of these mechanisms could then be tested in schizophrenia.

The last ten years has seen a great deal of activity in this field and we now know a good deal about the biochemical and pharmacological effects of LSD and mescalin. But we still do not know which, if any, of these mechanisms are actually responsible for their psychotomimetic effects in humans. The difficulties here are manifold. An important one is that these drugs have a large number of effects on different biochemical and pharmacological systems and it is difficult to distinguish between those that are necessary for the psychotomimetic effect and those that are merely fortuitous. One way round this difficulty is to do structure-activity relationship (SAR) studies. Close chemical analogs of the compound in question are synthesized. These are then tested both on the particular pharmacological or biochemical reaction concerned and also for their psychotomimetic effect. Certain compounds may show the same results in the biological rest as the standard compound and yet lack any psychotomimetic effect, in which case clearly the former was merely fortuitious. Only if we find constant correlation in a number of analogs between their biological activity and their psychotomimetic properties can we allot any significance to the former in the genesis of the latter. Furthermore the difficulties entailed in arguing from the results of animal experiments to human reactions must always be borne in mind together with the presence of marked species differences in biochemical and pharmacological reactions between animals.

3.2 EFFECTS ON ANIMAL BEHAVIOR

The extensive studies of Bradley and his school have shown that LSD and mescalin have an excitatory effect on both behavior and the EEG (Key and Bradley, 1960; Key , 1961). They have used conditioning techniques to override the effects of habituation to the response and they show that LSD increases arousal as evidenced by (a) decrease in the rate of extinction of a conditioned avoidance response (b) an increase in the range of generalized responses— e.g., to tones farther on the scale than the original one and to a decrease in the rate of extinction, and (c) to a fall in threshold (both as measured by EEG and behavioral responses) for an habituated conditioned stimulus. However, Evarts (1958) has introduced a complication into this neat picture by showing that the effect of LSD depends on the state of the cat at the beginning of the experiment. Diminution of arousal activity may be obtained in alert cats (at a dosage level of 50 - 100γ/kg.) whereas potentiation of arousal effects can be obtained in cats maintained in a quiet environment (at a dosage level of 500 γ/kg.). Elkes and Bradley had also previously emphasized the manner in which the effects of LSD depend on the nature of the immediate environment at the time. Maffii (1959) claims that mescalin (40 mg/kg.) and LSD (100 γ/kg) do not affect the rate of acquisition of unconditioned or primary conditioned reflexes but they accelerate the acquisition of secondary conditioned reflexes. The latter arise when the animal starts to give the response as soon as it is placed in the experimental box and before any stimuli are presented. These effects of LSD may be effected on the coliaterals from the main somatic afferent pathways into the reticular formation.

3.3 EFFECTS ON THE ELECTRICAL ACTIVITY OF THE BRAIN

The effects of LSD and mescalin have been tested on a number of electrical reactions of the brain including transmission through the lateral geniculate body, the cortical response evoked by sensory stimulation and various responses in the rhinecephalon. Evarts' report (1958) that low doses of LSD block synaptic transmission through the lateral geniculate nucleus has been confirmed by Bishop *et al.* (1959) who have filled in some more details about this effect. The block was not relieved by a fifteen second tetanus but was relieved by a ten minute one. This suggested that LSD acts by competitive inhibition of post-synaptic receptors. However, Bishop *et al.* (1958) had previously found that brom-LSD (non-hallucinogenic) also blocks synaptic transmission in the lateral geniculate body to some extent, so this property of LSD may not be relevant to its hallucinogenic properties in man.

Purpura (1956) has investigated the effect of LSD on the cortical potentials evoked by light flashes and by clicks. Small doses potentiated both the primary wave of the response as well as a smaller secondary one (the "W wave"), whereas higher doses inhibited both waves. He then investigated the effect of similar doses on recruiting responses evoked in the cerebral cortex by stimulation of the mid-line thalamic nuclei. These were inhibited by doses that facilitated the cortical response evoked by peripheral stimuli. He attempted to explain these results by formulating the hypothesis that LSD facilitates axosomatic synapses (mediating the specific response) and inhibiting axo-dendritic synapses (mediating recruiting responses). He tested this hypothesis by measuring the simultaneous response in the striate cortex to transcallosal (axo-dendritic) stimulation and to optic radiation (axo-somatic) stimulation. A dose of 25 γ/kg. markedly inhibited the former and facilitated the latter. Evarts (1958) also showed that large doses of LSD (1 mg/kg.) inhibited the cortical response to stimulation of the optic tract, but no effect was obtained following stimulation of the optic radiation— suggesting that the lateral geniculate body is concerned in this effect. However, Killam and Killam (1956) could not confirm the effect on the recruiting response and Evarts (1958) could only find an effect following very large doses. Possibly differences in anesthesia were responsible for these conflicting results.

A study of the action of mescalin on these responses has been made by Smythies *et al.* (1960). Mescalin seems to have an effect similar to LSD. The optic potential evoked in the cerebral cortex of the unanesthetized rabbit by a flash in the eye consists of a large primary response followed by some smaller waves. Small doses of mescalin potentiate the first two waves of this complex and reduce their variability in wave form. Large doses inhibit these waves. The smaller third and fourth waves in this response are depressed by all doses of mescalin used.

No work has as yet been done on the neurophysiological effects of the newly discovered hallucinogenic derivatives of HT and tryptamine. Amphetamine can be considered as a border-line psychotomimetic agent. With a single dose it induces only excitement and euphoria but not a psychosis as a true hallucinogen does. However, certain individuals react to prolonged ingestion of amphetamine by a clinical reaction that is indistinguishable from clinical paranoid schizophrenia. So what is lost on the swings is regained on the roundabouts for the clinical identity of the "model" and the natural psychosis may possibly argue a closer link between the biochemical mechanisms involved than may attain between the LSD reaction and schizophrenia. Amphetamine produces a powerful EEG and behavioral arousal, but in contrast to LSD, it affects the reticular formation directly.

Summary of Sections 3.2 and 3.3

It has recently been confirmed that LSD and mescalin have an excitant effect on the brain, both as measured by sophisticated behavioral methods involving conditioned responses and by EEG reactions. The effects of the two drugs have also been tested on a number of neurophysiological systems. LSD blocks synaptic transmission through the lateral geniculate body possibly by competitive inhibition of post-synaptic receptors. LSD and mescalin both potentiate, in small doses, the sensory evoked potential and inhibit it in larger doses. Amphetamine also produces EEG and behavioral arousal but probably acts at a different site to LSD.

3.4 PHARMACOLOGICAL AND BIOCHEMICAL EFFECTS

3.4A Peripheral Pharmacological Effects

LSD causes contraction of smooth muscle in various organs but its main effect is to inhibit the contractile effect of HT on smooth muscle. This action was the basis of the second specific biochemical hypothesis of schizophrenia. However, this anti-HT effect is also exerted by the non-psychotomimetic derivatives brom-LSD and d-1-methyl-lysergic acid monoethylamide and thus it cannot represent the central mechanism of action of LSD. Moreover mescalin does not have any peripheral anti-HT effect.

3.4B Central Pharmacological Effects

LSD has a number of effects on the central autonomic system some of which are sympathetic and some parasympathetic in nature. The sympathetic effects are exerted on the temperature regulating mechanism which is very sensitive to LSD. A rise in body temperature results. Hyperglycaemia, tachycardia, pilo-erection and mydriasis can also occur. These effects are blocked by adrenergic and ganglion blocking agents, chlorpromazine and general anesthetics. In some species some parasympathetic stimulation results—e.g., increased salivation and lacrimation are marked in the dog and brachycardia in the cat under certain conditions. This stimulation of the central autonomic system cannot be sufficient for its psychotomimetic effect for other LSD derivatives (such as lysergic acid dimethylamide and lysergic acid pyrrolidine) share these central vegetative stimulant effects but are only feebly hallucinogenic. However, most hallucinogenic drugs do act as central stimulants of the sympathetic system and so the psychotomimetic effect may depend on two factors both of which are necessary. For example, the psychosis could be produced by a particular action of the drug which can only operate when the sympathetic system is activated, possibly because the latter supplies the necessary biochemical basis for the former. In other words central sympathetic stimulation may be a necessary but not sufficient cause for psychotomimetic action and the second necessary factor may disturb the activated central sympathetic system in some particular way so that a psychotic reaction results.

Some more light has been shed recently on LSD-HT interactions in the brain and this has been shown to be more complex than was at first thought. For example, HT produces sedation in cats. This is antagonized by LSD but it is also antagonised by morphine and amphetamine which have no peripheral anti-HT action. Contrarywise the cats cannot be roused by brom-LSD which has peripheral anti-HT action, is not hallucinogenic and can certainly cross the blood-brain barrier. Furthermore, if the antagonism between LSD and HT is genuine, the reverse antagonism, i.e., of LSD effects by large doses of HT—should take place, which it does not. Vogt (1958) has shown that a most important but hitherto neglected factor is the exact locus in the brain where the interaction between HT and LSD takes place. By choosing one's locus correctly one can demonstrate a variety of modes of interaction. For example, the bulbar reticular formation, activated by HT, is depressed by LSD and the venteroposteromedial thalamic nucleus, depressed by HT, is activated by LSD. The venteromedial hypothalamic nucleus, depressed by HT is further depressed by LSD. Thus the effects of any drug on behavior cannot simply be expressed in terms of its action on the brain as a whole. It depends on the selective stimulation or inhibition of different centers by each drug. In this way all manner of complex effects may be mediated by inhibitors or other drugs that act on the same complex of centers. Sawyer (1957) has also demonstrated the importance of this. He gave the drugs via the intraventricular route to cats immobilized with flaxedil. The actions of LSD and HT were parallel and additive in certain subcortical structures, but their actions were opposite in the amygdala and putamen where LSD stimulated activity and HT depressed it. Olds (1958), using his technique whereby rats can stimulate their own brains electrically, has also confirmed this. With the electrodes located in most parts of the brain LSD abolishes all self-stimulation for a short time. This effect of LSD is antagonised by HT in the case of the septal area and the pre-optic and posterior regions of the hypothalamus. It is not so antagonised when the electrodes are placed in the ventral regions below the septal area and the ventral parts of the middle hypothalamus. Thus clearly the central effects of LSD, HT and similar drugs is a most complex affair and must depend not only on the particular anatomical loci involved but also presumably on the functional state of the neurones and glia at each locus at the time of administration.

It has been established (Sankar *et al.*, 1961b) that LSD raises levels of HT in the whole brain (by 40%) and induces a large increase in the rate of turn over of HT (to 350%). Freedman (1961) showed that this effect of LSD is not shared by its psychiatrically inactive relatives l-LSD and brom-LSD. As LSD does not increase the rate of formation or destruction of HT either *in vivo* or *in vitro*, Freedman suggests that LSD probably stimulates binding of brain HT to its stored form. Thus it would work in a manner directly the reverse of reserpine. Thus it may be that the hallucinogenic properties of LSD and its congeners are not related to their peripheral anti-HT effects but are related to their power to bind HT centrally.

Brodie (1958) has put forword the hypothesis that LSD acts by depressing the trophotropic (parasympathetic) system by competing with HT at its active site. It may also work by stimulating active sites of the ergotrophic (sympathetic) system. Or perhaps both these are necessary at the same time. LSD has built into its chemical structure the skeleton of an HT or psilocybin-like indole and it is also a phenylethylamine derivative. Brodie's more general hypothesis is that HT acts as the trophotropic synaptic transmitter (or perhaps rather modulates synaptic function) and that norepinephrine fulfills the same role for the ergotrophic system. Curtis and Koizumi (1961), using multibarrelled microelectrodes, claim that neither HT nor nor-epinephrine have any synaptic action in various parts of the mesencephalic reticular system that they examined. Brodie (1962) criticises their conclusions on the grounds that they ignore the effect of synaptic barriers which may prevent the ready diffusion of the active agent to their proper site of action. Furthermore he suggests that the HT and nor-epinephrine should have been given under cover of a mono-amine oxidase inhibitor (MAOI); otherwise it cannot be claimed that the amines survive long enough to have any effect. Brodie backs up these criticisms with some experimental evidence. Mice treated with MAOI and a compound that specifically releases brain nor-epinephrine (but not HT) from its storage sites and therefore into its natural receptors, exhibit a very strong amphetamine-like excitation. This type of experiment obviates the difficulties that the drug may fail to cross the blood-brain barrier or may act at sites other than its usual one.

3.4C Biochemical Effects

Certain *in vitro* studies have been carried out on the effect of LSD and mescalin on various enzyme systems but Bain (1957) concludes that none of these throw any light on the problem of the mechanism of their psychomimetic action. For example LSD is a powerful inhibitor of human brain and serum pseudocholinesterase and it is much less active against these enzymes in the brains of rats and other animals. This led to the idea that this might be connected with its hallucinogenic powers. But structure-activity relationship studies have shown that this cannot be so. For the psychiatrically quite inactive stereo-isomers of LSD (l-LSD and d-iso-LSD) as well as brom-LSD all inhibit the enzyme to a greater extent than do a series of psychotomimetic relatives of LSD (such as d-l-methyl-LSD) (Zsigmond *et al.*, 1961).

The action of mescalin has also been studied on some cerebral enzymes. In most cases the large doses used render any deductions from the results of dubious worth. However Lewis and McIlwain (1954) used electrically stimulated slices of guinea-pig cortex and reported that mescalin (10^{-3} M) inhibited (by 50%) only that increment of respiration produced by the electrical stimulation. LSD had the same effect. Scheuler (1948) had previously claimed that mescalin will inhibit cerebral respiration only if it is incubated with the material for two and one half to three hours beforehand. Tsunoda's recent results (1960) have confused this picture since he finds that mescalin (10^{-3} M; 3×10^{-3} M) does not inhibit the increment of respiration of isolated cortex produced by electrical stimulation. However, after the period of stimulation the uptake of oxygen did fall to lower levels in the mescalinized slices than in the controls. This fall took place from two and one half to three hours after adding the mescalin in keeping with Scheuler's results. Similar results were reported by Quastel and Wheatley (1933) using 4×10^{-3} M dosage of mescalin. Further work is clearly needed on this problem.

At present we know that mescalin does not affect oxaloacetic or oxalosuccinic carboxylases or transaminases (Block, Block and Patzig, 1952b), nor succinic dehydrogenase or cytochrome oxidase (Clark *et al.*, 1954). Nor does it have any effect on the uptake of oxygen or on phosphorylation in preparations of mitochondria of rat brain respiring *in vitro* on a pyruvate substrate (Bain, 1957). Adrenochrome is a powerful inhibitor of glycolysis in brain tissue (Randall, 1946). It probably inhibits the phosphate transfer mechanism of the glyolytic cycle. Meyerhof and Randall (1948) showed that this was accompanied by inhibition of hexokinase and phosphohexokinase (50% inhibition at the low concentration of 4×10^{-5} M). Adrenochome is also very active in other respects. Radsma and Golterman (1954) showed that it will stimulate the oxidation of ascorbic acid (at 10^{-6} M) and will inhibit the oxidation of lactates (at 10^{-4} M). Park *et al.* (1956) found that 5×10^{-4} M adrenochrome will completely uncouple oxidative phosphorylation in hamster liver mitochondria respiring on β-hydroxybutyrate. In this regard Geiger's observation (1960) that adrenochrome is extremely toxic to neurones grown in tissue culture is of importance. However, Geronimus *et al.* (1956) measured the effect of LSD and some of its relatives on the oxygen uptake of minced guinea-pig brain. Brom-LSD and l-LSD (both psychiatrically inactive) were as effective as LSD in inhibiting respiration. Therefore this activity cannot be sufficient for hallucinogenic activity.

Recently the interesting discovery has been made that certain steroids counter some of the effects of LSD. Prednisone reduces LSD-induced anxiety (Abramson and Sklarofsky, 1960) and pro-gesterone counters the effect of LSD on rat behavior and on various psychological tests in humans (Bergen *et al.*, 1960a). A further point of interest is that Denber (1959) has shown the anti-parkinson phenothiazine derivative diethazine potentiates the mescalin psychosis in man. This may be due to the N.N.-diethylamine side chain of diethazine. It has recently been demonstrated (Takahashi and Akabane, 1960) that chronic administration of methampheta-mine to rats for a period of twenty-five to fifty-seven days (at 6mg/kg.) leads to a significant reduction of brain hexokinase activity. They report that brain hexokinase activity was similarly dimin-ished in a few brain biopsy specimens from schizophrenic patients.

3.4D Structure-activity Relationships

Further studies of the mode of action of these drugs may be carried out by altering the molecule in some systematic way and observing the effect of the change in molecular structure on its biological effects. In this way information may be deduced as to the molecular configuration of the receptor site at which the drug exerts its effects. In the case of LSD the extensive studies of the Sandoz group have shown the remarkable molecular specificity necessary for its effects. Firstly the stereoisometric specificity is complete. Only the d-form is active and the other three steroisomers (l-LSD, d-iso LSD and l-iso LSD) are completely inactive. The substitution of bromine at R2 (Fig. 6) abolishes all activity. Substitution of an acetyl group at R1 does not affect psychotomimetic activity but a methyl group here reduces it by some 60 per cent. Any change in the side chain grouping reduces activity. Lysergic acid monoethylamide has only 5 per cent of the activity of LSD itself; the dimethylamide 10 per cent; the pyrrolidide 10 per cent, the morpholide 20 per cent. Combinations of substitution on the ring at R1 and alterations of the side chain tend to reduce activity still further. However no deductions from this work as to the possible nature of the receptor site involved have as yet been made.

Less work has been done in the case of mescalin. Peretz *et al.* (1955) showed that α-methylation of mescalin increases its psychotomimetic powers in humans by a factor of about 2. This result has recently been confirmed by Shulgin *et al.* (1961). They used somewhat larger doses and observed extreme mental derangement and,

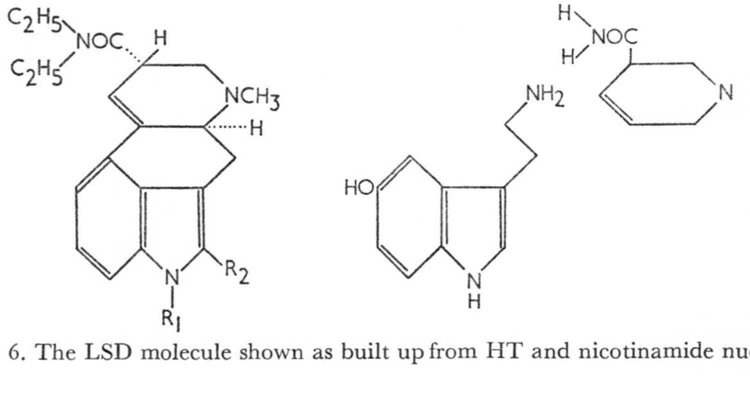

Fig. 6. The LSD molecule shown as built up from HT and nicotinamide nuclei.

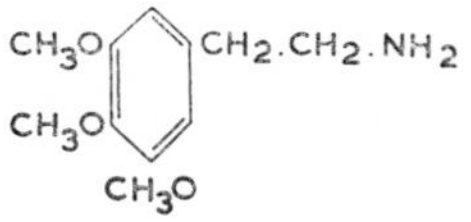

Fig. 7. Mescalin analogs described in text.

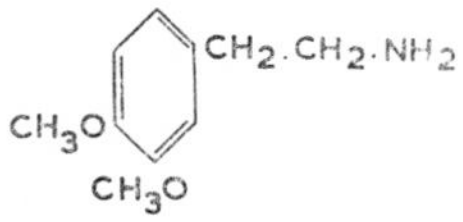

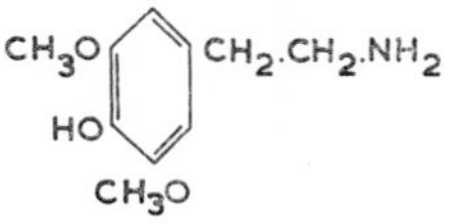

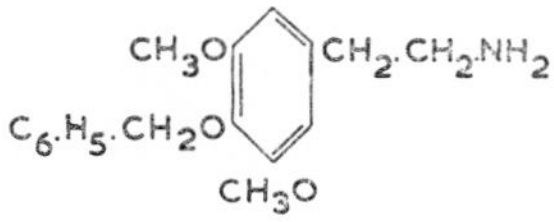

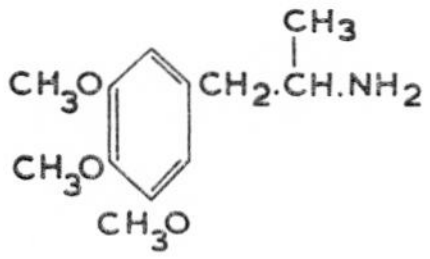

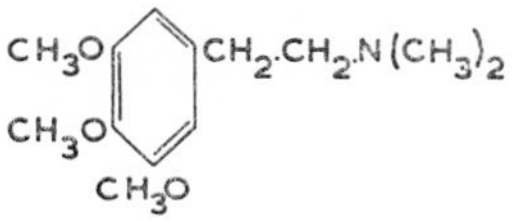

in particular, anger, hostility and megalomaniacal euphoria—an effect not seen previously in these same subjects under LSD or mescalin. This may however be a quantitative rather than a qualitative matter due to the greater relative potency of α-methyl mescalin (V, Fig. 7). This compound is chemically very interesting since it represents a fusion of the mescalin and the amphetamine molecules, i.e., besides being α-methylmescalin it is 3, 4, 5-tri-methoxyamphetamine. Another neglected compound is N. N. dimethylmescalin (or tricocereine) (VI, Fig. 7). In view of the great increase in psychotomimetic activity produced by the N.N. dimethylation of serotonin and tryptamine (both of which have the same side-chain as mescalin), it is of interest to note that the sole report on tricocereine in the literature is by Lúdueña (1935) who bravely ingested some 550 mgs. of the compound without any effects "que una ligera pesadez gástrica." Smythies and Levy (1960) tested a number of mescalin analogs on the Winter and Flataker rat rope climbing test. In this the rat learns to climb a rope to get a food reward. The time that the rat takes to climb the rope is measured. Mescalin slows down the climbing time of the rats (50mg./kg. has a marked effect). If we remove one methoxy group to produce 3.4. dimethoxyphenylethylamine (II, Fig. 7) the activity is reduced by one-half. If we replace the methoxy group in the 4 position of mescalin by an hydroxyl group (III, Fig. 7) all activity is abolished; if we replace it by a benzyloxy group (IV, Fig. 7) the activity is increased about two-fold. However, it must be noted that the effects of mescalin in such tests demanding a marked motor response from the rat is contaminated by the recent observation (Schopp *et al.*, 1961) that mescalin has a direct curare-like effect on muscle. Alles (1957) reported that 3.4. methylenedioxyphenylethylamine has no hallucinogenic properties but that the corresponding isopropylamine derivative has (in a dose of 126 mg.). Clearly, again, only the surface of this problem has been scratched and much more work will have to be done in this field of SAR before we can make any deductions about the possible configurations of the receptor sites at which these drugs induce their effects. In this context Vane (1960) reports that mescalin is peculiar amongst amines in that it has the properties of a type 3 sympatheticomimetic amine on tryptamine receptors in the rat stomach strip, but it has no effect, as do other type 3 amines (e.g., HT) on the chemoreceptors that induce brachycardia and apnea in the lightly anesthetized rat. Some SAR studies on the hallucinogenic tryptamine derivatives will be discussed in Section 3.6.

3.5 ENDOCRINOLOGICAL EFFECTS

LSD appears to stimulate the pituitary-adrenal axis (Rinkel *et al.*, 1955) with resulting changes in blood and urinary constituents. Hoagland (1957) reviews some important biochemical similarities between schizophrenics and normal people who have taken LSD. After the initial stimulation of the pituitary-adrenal axis LSD subjects become relatively unresponsive to most of the effects of ACTH. Both groups excrete abnormally low amounts of inorganic phosphate but after the injection of ACTH they excrete much more than do controls. This suggests that both LSD and the unknown metabolic disturbance of schizophrenia facilitate the retention of inorganic phosphorus. However, a more recent study (Koch *et al.*, 1961) suggests that a modification of this conclusion should be made. These workers could only differentiate between schizophrenics and non-schizophrenics on a basis of ACTH-induced phosphaturia when cortisone was used and the means of the results obtained over a three day period compared. Other workers (Ganong *et al.*, 1961) failed to demonstrate any effect of LSD 50 γ/kg in dogs on adrenal responsiveness to ACTH nor on the sensitivity of the pituitary-adrenal axis to stress.

Arnold and Hoffman (1961) find that a large dose of succinic acid produces a disturbance in the proportions of inorganic and esterified phosphate in schizophrenic, but not in depressed patients. These changes were also found in the relatives of schizophrenics. (these authors do not give any further details of their findings in this abstract). Sankar *et al.* (1961a) report that erythrocytes and plasma from schizophrenic children contain more inorganic and less esterified phosphate than normal. The uptake of labelled serotonin by their platelets was also less. LSD also increases serum inorganic phosphate. These findings seem to be in line with those of Hoagland and his group.

Summary of Sections 3.4 and 3.5

The hallucinogenic drugs, particularly LSD, have been shown to be potent pharmacological agents with a variety of effects. Some of these seem not to be sufficient for hallucinogenic activity but they may be essential part causes. For instance a peripheral anti-HT action is shared by (active) LSD and (inactive) brom-LSD but it is not possessed by (active) mescalin. Therefore it is probably neither necessary nor sufficient for psychotomimetic action. Most hallucinogens stimulate the central sympathetic system. LSD has complex modes of interaction with HT in the brain. They are synergistic in some regions and antagonistic in others. One effect that does correlate with hallucinogenic activity is the raising of brain levels and rates of turnover of HT. Another is its effect in potentiating some peripheral actions of epinephrine. The anti-cholinesterase activity of LSD and its analogs is not correlated with their hallucinogenic effect: some psychiatrically inactive compounds are as active as LSD, whereas mescalin is inactive. The effect of these agents on the biochemical mechanisms of the brain is still not yet worked out. We know a number of enzymes that mescalin does not affect. Our knowledge of their effect on the oxygen uptake of the brain has recently become confused by conflicting results and by the fact that brom-LSD and other psychiatrically inactive agents have also been reported to inhibit respiration. Some recent work relevant to Brodie's hypothesis of the role of HT and nor-epinephrine in the brain has been discussed. The important research method of structure-activity relationships has been applied fairly extensively to LSD but as yet no deductions have been made from these data to the possible configuration of the receptor sites at which LSD may operate. Some work in this line has been done on mescalin. Recent findings in the endocrinological changes in schizophrenia implicates changes in phosphate metabolism thus linking up with the work on carbohydrate metabolism described above.

3.6 NEWER HALLUCINOGENIC AGENTS

The recent finding of psychotomimetic derivatives of serotonin and tryptamine has been of particular importance. Bufotenin (N.N. dimethyl HT) (II, Fig. 8) causes violent vegetative effects and some mental changes but it is doubtful if it is a true hallucinogen (Turner and Merlis, 1959). It does however disrupt

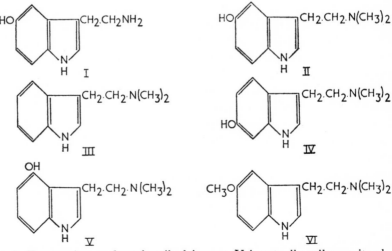

Fig. 8. Tryptamine analogs described in text. V is actually psilocyn. its phosphoric acid ester is psilocybin.

the performance of trained rats in the Winter and Flataker test and it shows some cross-tolerance with LSD (Mahler and Humoller, 1959). It is found in nature in a variety of loci including cohoba, an hallucinogenic snuff from Haiti. Then two synthetic compounds were discovered in Hungary (Böszörményi, 1961)—dimethyltryptamine (DMT) (III, Fig. 8) and diethyltryptamine (DET). DMT produces violent vegetative symptoms and a typical mescalin-like psychosis which subsides after only one hour as compared to the eight to ten hours that the psychosis induced by mescalin endures. DET produces a similar result lasting three hours. The dibutyl derivative has a very weak action and the dihexyl one is inactive. These reactions appear to correlate with the ease with which these compounds can be 6-hydroxylated. The 6-OH derivatives are thought by Szara and Rockland (1961), to be the actual hallucinogenic agents in the body. (IV, Fig. 8). Lastly psilocybin (V, Fig. 8), which is a phosphoric acid ester of 4-hydroxy-N.N.-dimethyltryptamine, was discovered in the small Mexican mushroom *Psilocybe mexicana Heim* by Heim and Hofmann (1958). This compound produces an effect very similar to that induced by DET. Chemically it is of interest as it and the derivatives of lysergic acid are the only naturally occurring indoles substituted in the 4-position. Pharmacologically it has the LSD-like property of central sympathetic stimulation (but to a lesser degree) (Cerletti, 1959) as evidenced by pupillary dilatation, tachycardia and pyrexia. It is about one hundred fold less active an anti-HT agent on rat uterus than LSD. It also causes retention of inorganic phosphate (Hollister, 1961).

A most important discovery by Axelrod (1961) has been of a N-methylating enzyme in mammalian tissue (rabbit lung) that will actually convert serotonin to bufotenin and tryptamine into DMT. Thus, metabolic pathways have actually been demonstrated in a mammalian tissue whereby potent psychotomimetic agents could be synthesized. The importance of N-methylation (DMT, psilocybin, bufotenin) and O-methylation (mescalin) suggests the possible mechanism by which methionine exacerbates the symptoms of schizophrenics (Pollin *et al.*, 1961). Fischer *et al.* (1961) have reported the isolation by using chromatographic techniques of a bufotenin-like substance from the urine of 25/26 schizophrenics. This result seems rather improbable for schizophrenics do not show any of the marked vegetative features of bufotenin poisoning. Perhaps, however, the presence of small quantities of bufotenin, themselves ineffectual, indicate the occurrence of a wider metabolic upset which would itself be the causative agent. Brune and Himwich (1963) have recently confirmed the presence of bufotenin in small quantities in schizophrenic urine (about 30 γ. per urine sample). They were unable to detect the presence of any other N.N.-dimethylated compounds. Further additions of methyl groups to the ring structure of these N.N.-dimethyl derivatives (e.g., by converting 5-hydroxy-N.N.-dimethyl tryptamine to 5-methoxy-N:N:-dimethyl tryptamine; or HT to 5-methoxy-HT) increases their capacity to disrupt learned behavior in rats, (Gessner, 1961). 5-methoxy-DMT was the most active tryptamine derivative Gessner tested. 19 $\mu M/kg$ produced as great a reaction as $4\mu M/kg$ LSD with a much quicker onset: in the former the disruption reached its median value in 1.8 minutes and in the case of the latter in 6.3 minutes (intraperitoneal injection). DMT and DET were less effective at a larger dose and 5-benzoxy-DMT was even less effective.

Summary of 3.6

The importance of the newly discovered hallucinogenic derivatives of tryptamine has been stressed. It lies in the demonstration of the narrow chemical gap between chemicals that are active in brain biochemistry on the one hand and powerful hallucinogenic agents on the other. It seems unlikely that this fact has no bearing on the problem of the etiology of schizophrenia and other psychoses. This is particularly so since the enzyme needed to effect the necessary change to cross this gap has been isolated in mammalian tissues. The importance of excess methylation in this respect has been demonstrated by two different methods.

3.7 DISCUSSION OF FUTURE WORK IN THIS FIELD

Enough leads have now been uncovered and shown to be reasonable and heuristically fruitful to keep a larger number of research workers busy for a long time. The nature of the toxic factor in the globulin fraction from schizophrenic plasma needs intensive investigation as do the reported abnormalities in intermediate carbohydrate metabolism, tryptophane metabolism, the real significance of the effects of feeding methionine to schizophrenic patients, the disorders in the immunity reaction, etc.

Secondly, many more studies are needed on the basic biochemical and neurophysiological mechanisms underlying psychosis. At present this would entail an intensive study of the biochemical, neuropharmacological and neurophysiological effects of the known hallucinogenic drugs and in particular their effect on the reactivity and metabolism of their closely related analogs present in the brain. In any such work it is most important not to test the effect of just one drug on the particular system under study. If we are to disentangle unimportant side-effects from the important causal effects we must test a series of drugs including both psychotomimetic and non-psychotomimetic analogs of the drug in question. We should also test hallucinogens belonging to another series and their psychotomimetic and non-psychotomimetic analogs. All these compounds need testing on a number of biological test systems including enzymes, different aspects of the electrical activity of the brain and different aspects of behavior. Then their neuropharmacological interaction with the effects of possible neurohumors, or modulators of neurohumors, such as HT, nor-epinephrine, acetylcholine, etc., needs working out in detail. When this mass of data has been obtained we will not only be able to correlate psychotomimetic activity with the basic neurobiological properties of the molecules; we will also be able to contribute to basic neuropharmacology. This is because this sort of study also yields data that correlates neurobiological activity at different levels. That is to say we are not only studying these drugs themselves. The same experimental design also enables us to use them in the same experiments, as research tools. For instance if all drugs that inhibit a certain enzyme system A also inhibit a certain electrical reaction B and those drugs that do not inhibit A do not inhibit B either, then we may deduce, as a working hypothesis, that the electrical reaction B is mediated in some way by the chemical reaction A. In this way the same research will provide data useful to basic neurobiological research as well as data directly useful to psychiatry merely by using different correlations within the same mass of data.

Section 4

CHEMICAL ASPECTS OF
THE TREATMENT OF SCHIZOPHRENIA

THIS section is concerned only with what is known about the chemical treatment of schizophrenia. Thus, it is unavoidably short as very little is known in this field. However, a few facts of interest and importance have emerged.

Unlike general medicine with its many drugs effective against disease, psychiatry relies on singularly few. In schizophrenia the only treatment for decades was insulin shock therapy which is now hardly used at all. In any event nothing is known about how it works or even if it ever worked in any specific manner, at all (Ackner and Oldham, 1962). Social and psychotherapeutic measures remain of course important. The main task here is to remove the social stigma that still attaches, in our culture, to schizophrenia. One can argue that one effective method of doing this would be to demonstrate the particular biochemical mechanism that is at fault in the illness so as to give a tolerant public opinion something concrete around which to crystallize. Furthermore, as we know more about the causes of an illness, so more effective treatment will be evolved. Eventually most cases of schizophrenia will probably be treated as outpatients or as such following a short stay in hospital. As the clinical picture of the treated disease and the prognosis improve so will the cultural response towards it.

Current chemical therapy of schizophrenia is based almost entirely upon the phenothiazine group of compounds. The original member of the group—chlorpromazine—is still widely used. The basic chemical nucleus involved is shown in Figure 9 and different drugs in this series are produced by substitution at the R_1 and R_2 positions. The phenothiazines fall into three subgroups:

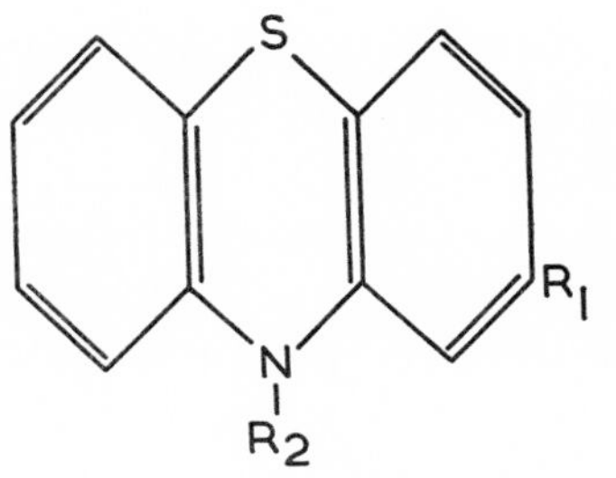

Fig. 9. The phenothiazine nucleus.

(A) R_2 is a dimethylaminopropane chain. If, then R_1 is a chlorine atom chlorpromazine results and if it is a $-CF_3$ group trifluopromazine or vesprin result:

(B) In some the side chain at R_2 contains a piperazine ring. This with R_1 = Cl gives prochlorperazine (stemetil, compazine) and with R_1 = $-CF_3$ gives trifluoperazine (stelazine). A minor change in the side chain of this and R_1 = Cl gives perphenazine (trilafon, fentazine) and with R_1 = $-CF_3$ gives fluphenazine (moditen). In general the drugs in group B are more powerful than those in group A. They are less toxic to the liver and marrow but produce extrapyramidal syndromes to a greater extent. Those with the $-CF_3$ grouping are more powerful than those with the chlorine atom in the R_1 position.

(c) In this group the side chain contains a piperidine ring. The most useful is Thioridazine (Melleril) where R_1 = CH_3.

These drugs all, to varying degrees, combat excited, psychotic behavior, and reduce anxiety, delusions, hallucinations and other symptoms of schizophrenia. They will usually produce great improvement in attacks of acute schizophrenic illness but they have less effect on the more chronic conditions and in cases of hebephrenic and simple schizophrenia. In many cases the drugs will produce a symptomatic cure in that the patient will act and feel normally while he is on the drugs but will soon relapse if he is taken off them.

A great deal of work remains to be done to determine the mode of action of these drugs. This is not to deny that a good deal of work has already been done, mainly on chlorpromazine, but it is still true to say that we do not really know how they work. It will be recalled, however, that one common and major effect of the hallucinogenic drugs is to stimulate sympathetic centers in the brain and so raise sympathetic tone throughout the body. Chlorpromazine has the opposite effect and lowers sympathetic tone mainly by a central action. In animals, central sympathetic stimulation (such as may be produced by DOPA, amphetamine, ephedrine and LSD) induces a syndrome characterised by increased alertness, increased motor activity, greater attention to external stimuli, increased respiration and a rise in body temperature. Chloropromazine produces the opposite effect on all these functions and moreover the effects of the two groups of drugs directly counteract each other. Its central action is demonstrated by the fact that doses too small to be effective systematically are fully active if injected intrathecally or into the carotid artery (Spector *et al.*, 1957; Jourdan *et al.*, 1955). It may act by selectively antagonizing the effect of nor-epinephrine in the C.N.S., Chlorpromazine readily enters the brain and, unlike reserpine, is rapidly effective and its effects do not outlast its physical presence in the nervous system. It is also rapidly and totally metabolized with the production of a sulphoxide. A prominent feature of the phenothiazines, particularly those of group B, is to produce a variety of extrapyramidal syndromes. This may possibly be correlated with the large amounts of dopamine that are such a characteristic feature of the corpus striatum.

Chlorpromazine does not have any marked effect on thresholds for the arousal response elicited by direct stimulation of the reticular formation but it effectively blocks arousal produced by afferent stimulation (Bradley and Key, 1958). It does not affect the primary projection pathways and thus it probably acts at the same locus as does LSD; i.e., the afferent collaterals from this system into the reticular formation. They may both work by their effect on the activity of nor-epinephrine at this site, but in the opposite sense. Reserpine does not have these effects on the reticular formation but it, not chlorpromazine, does affect the amygdala where it initiates spontaneous electrical seizure patterns, which may spread to other parts of the rhinencephalon but not to the cerebral cortex (Sigg and Schneider, 1957).

Phenothiazines also block the conditioned avoidance response. Chlorpromazine has an ED 50 of 11.9 mg./kg. and trifluoperazine one of 1.2 mg./kg.—a ratio that reflects their therapeutic dosage ratio in clinical practice. This effect is produced at a dosage that does not produce ataxia or prostration. Other agents, such as meprobamate or barbiturates produce only a non-specific block of this response at dosages which produce ataxia and prostration. Chlorpromazine also affects various basic mechanisms as follows: it reduces the uptake of aromatic aminoacids by the brain and permeation to and from their storage depots (Pletscher and Gey, 1961). It decreases the permeability of membranes to certain substances and certain brain areas concentrate it (particularly the hypothalamus and also hypochondria). The release of acetyl choline from synaptic vesicles is inhibited by 5×10^{-6} chlorpromazine (Guth and Sprites, 1961). Chlorpromazine also effectively blocks the action of mescaline as a psychotomimetic agent.

Reserpine has also been used in the treatment of schizophrenia in the past. It produces a clinical state of tranquilization very similar to that produced by chlorpromazine but it acts on a different central mechanism. For example, chlorpromazine depresses the central sympathetic system whereas reserpine stimulates the central parasympathetic system, and so produces its well known effects of miosis, lacrymation and salivation. The lowered sympathetic activity induced by reserpine is due to loss of epinephrine from its peripheral stores (Carlsson *et al.*, 1957a). The basic mode of action of reserpine is to deplete stores of HT and norepinephrine. These therefore, although quickly synthesized, are as rapidly destroyed by MAO. Furthermore reserpine does not antagonize the central excitation produced by LSD and amphetamine and it aggravates the LSD psychosis. As for its central sedative effects it is now certain that it acts by depletion of HT and not norepinephrine. This was discovered by the use of an agent (α-methyl-m-tyrosine) which selectively depletes norepinephrine and not HT. If it is given to mice no sedation results. If then reserpine is given which depletes the HT remaining, sedation ensues (Kuntzman *et al.*, 1961). Similar experiments suggested that the excitation, produced in mice by giving a MAOI together with reserpine, is associated with a rise in brain levels of free norepinephrine. However Carlsson *et al.* (1957b) have shown the HT precursor 5HTP (to 1000 mg./kg.) could not overcome the sedation induced reserpine whereas the norepinephrine precursor—3.4 DOPA (500-1000 mg./kg.) produced a dramatic response.

Thus it is most interesting to note that drugs which 'cure' psychosis have close connections with certain key chemicals in the brain, namely HT and norepinephrine. One factor that seems to contribute to the development of psychosis is an overactive or morbidly active central sympathetic system. This may be combatted by a drug such as chlorpromazine which reduces activity in this system or by a drug such as reserpine which stimulates the antagonistic parasympathetic system. Even if HT and norepinephrine are not central synaptic transmitting agents, they must have some important influence over the activity in these systems. The hallucinogenic and tranquilizing drugs seem to exert many of their most important effects on these systems and disorders in their chemistry may be at the root of schizophrenia.

REFERENCES

Abramson, H. A. and Skarlofsky, B.: "Lysergic acid diethylamide (LSD-25) antagonists." *A.M.A. Arch. gen. Psychiat.*, 2:89, 1960.

Ackner, B. and Oldham, A. J.: "Insulin treatment of schizophrenia." *Lancet*, 504, March 10th, 1962.

Alles, G.: "Some relations between chemical structure and physiological action of mescaline and related compounds." *Neuropsychopharmacology.* Transactions of the Fourth Conference. New York, Josiah Macy, Jr. Foundation, 1957.

Altschule, M. D.: *Bodily Physiology in Mental and Emotional Disorders.* New York, Grune & Stratton, 1953.

Anastasopoulos, G. and Photiades, H.: "Effects of LSD in relatives of schizophrenic patients." *J. Ment. Sci.*, 108:95, 1962.

Armstrong, M. D., McMillan, A. and Shaw, K. N. F.: "3-methoxy-4-hydroxy-D-mandelic acid, a urinary metabolite of norepinephrine." *Biochem. et Biophys. Acta.*, 25:422, 1957.

Arnold, O. H. and Hoffman, G.: "Results of a biochemical test-method for the diagnosis of schizophrenic psychoses and their hereditary taint." Abst. IIIrd World Congress Psychiat., Montreal, 1961, p. 204.

Ashcroft, G.: Personal communication, 1962.

Axelrod, B.: "Other pathways of carbohydrate metabolism." *Metabolic Pathways*, 1:205, 1960.

Axelrod, J.: "Enzymatic formation of psychotomimetic metabolites from normally occurring compounds." *Science*, 134:343, 1961.

Axelrod, J. and Tomchick, R.: "Enzymatic O-methylation of epinephrine and other catechols." *J. Biol. Chem.*, 233:702, 1958.

Bain, J. A.: "A review of the biochemical effects *in vitro* of certain psychotomimetic agents." *Ann. New York Acad. Sci.*, 66:459, 1957.

Bang, O.: "The lactate content of the blood during and after muscular exercise in man." *Skand. Arch. fur Physiol.*, 4:Suppl., 10:51, 1936.

Benassi, C. A., Benassi, P., Allegri, G. and Ballarin, P.: "Tryptophan metabolism in schizophrenic patients." *J. Neurochem.*, 7:264, 1961.

Benedict, R.: *Patterns of Culture.* London, Routledge, 1935.

61

Bercel, N. A.: "The effect of schizophrenic blood on the behavior of spiders." In *Neuropsychopharmacology* edited by P. B. Bradley, P. Deniker, and C. Radouco-Thomas, Elsevier, Amsterdam, 1959.

Bergen, J. R., Krus, D. and Pincus, G.: "Suppression of LSD-25 effects in rats by steroids." *Proc. Soc. exp. Biol. Med.*, *105:*254, 1960a.

Bergen, J. R., Pennell, R. B., Freeman, H., Hoagland, H. and Smythies, J. R.: "Rat behavior changes in response to a blood factor from normal and psychotic persons." *A.M.A. Arch. Neurol.*, *2:*146, 1960b.

Bergen, J. R., Koella, W. P., Czicman, J. and Hoagland, H.: "Evoked optic potential changes induced by plasma globulins from schizophrenics." *Fed. Proc.*, *20:*305, 1961.

Bernstein, J., Mazur, W. P. and Walaszek, E. J.: "The histaminolytic activity of serum from schizophrenic patients." *Med. Exp.* (Basel), *2:* 239, 1960.

Bishop, M. P.: "Effect of schizophrenic plasma upon original learning in the rat." *Dis. Nerv. Syst.*, *21:*133, 1960.

Bishop, P. O., Burke, W. and Hayhow, W. R.: "Lysergic acid diethylamide block of lateral geniculate synapses and relief by repetitive stimulation." *Exp. Neurol.*, *1:*556, 1959.

Bishop, P. O., Field, G., Hennessey, B. L. and Smith, J. R.: "Action of d-lysergic acid diethylamide on lateral geniculate synapses." *J. Neurophysiol.*, *21:*529, 1958.

Block, W., Block, K. and Patzig, B.: "Zur physiologie des C^{14}-radioaktiven Mescalins im Tierversuch. II. Verteilung der Radioaktivatat in den organen in Abhangigkeit von der Zeit." *Hoppe-Seyler's Zeitschr. physiol. Chem.*, *290:*230, 1952a.

Block, W., Block, K. and Patzig, B.: "Zur physiologie des C^{14}-radioaktiven Mescalins in Tierversuch. III. Mescalineinbau in Leberprotein." *Hoppe-Seyler's Zeitschr. physiol. Chem.*, *291:*119, 1952b.

Bloom, B., Stetten, M. R. and Stetten, D., Jr.: "Evaluation of catabolic pathways of glucose in mammalian systems." *J. Biol. Chem.*, *204:*681, 1953.

Bogoch, S., Dussik, K. T. and Lever, P. G.: "Clinical status and cerebrospinal fluid 'Total neuraminic acid'." *A.M.A. Arch. gen. Psychiat.*, *1:* 441, 1959.

Bogoch, S., Dussik, K. T., Fender, C. and Conran, P.: "Longitudinal clinical and neurochemical studies on schizophrenic and manic-depressive psychoses." *Amer. J. Psychiat.*, *117:*409, 1960.

Böszörményi, Z.: "Psilocybin and diethyltryptamine. Two tryptamine hallucinogens." In *Neuropsychopharmacology*. Vol. 2 edited by E. Rothlin, Elservier, Amsterdam, 226, 1961.

Boszormenyi-Nagy, I. and Gerty, F. J.: "Diagnostic aspects of study of intracellular phosphorylations in schizophrenia." *Amer. J. Psychiat.*, *112*:11, 1955.

Braceland, F. J., Meduna, L. J. and Vaichulis, J. A.: "Delayed action of insulin in schizophrenia." *Amer. J. Psychiat.*, *102*:108, 1945.

Bradley, P. B. and Key, B. J.: "The effect of drugs on arousal responses produced by electrical stimulation of the reticular formation of the brain." *E.E.G. Clin. Neurophysiol.*, *10*:97, 1958.

Brodie, B. B.: "Storage and release of 5-hydroxytryptamine," in *5-Hydroxytryptamine*, edited by G. P. Lewis, Pergamon Press, London, 1958, p. 64.

Brodie, B. B.: Personal communication, 1962.

Brown, F. C., White, J. B. and Kennedy, J. K.: "Urinary excretion of tryptophan metabolites by schizophrenic individuals." *Amer. J. Psychiat.*, *117*:63, 1960.

Brune, G. G. and Himwich, H. E.: "Indole metabolism in schizophrenic patients." *A.M.A. Arch. gen. Psychiat.*, *6*:82, 1962.

Brune, G. G. and Himwich, H. E.: "Biogenic amines and behavior in schizophrenic patients." In *Recent Advances in Biological Psychiatry*, Vol. 5. In press, 1963.

Cardon, P. V., Sokoloff, L., Vates, T. S. and Kety, S. S.: "The physiological and psychological effects of intravenously administered epinephrine and its metabolism in normal and schizophrenic men. I. Effects on heart rate, blood pressure, blood glucose concentration and the electroencephalogram." *J. Psychiat. Res.*, *1*:37, 1961.

Carlsson, A., Rosengren, E., Bertler, A. and Nilsson, J.: "Effect of reserpine on the metabolism of catechol amines." In *Psychotropic Drugs*, edited by S. Garattini, Amsterdam, Elsevier, 1957a, p. 363.

Carlsson, A., Lindqvist, M. and Magnusson, T.: "3,4-dihydroxyphenylalanine and 5-hydroxytryptophan as reserpine antagonists." *Nature*, *180*:1200, 1957b.

Cerletti, A.: "Pharmacology of psilocybin." In *Neuro-Psychopharmacology*, edited by P. B. Bradley, P. Deniker and C. Radouco-Thomas, Elsevier, Amsterdam, 1959, p. 291.

Christoni, G. and Zappoli, R.: "Neuraminic acids in the cerebrospinal fluid of schizophrenic and oligophrenic patients." *Amer. J. Psychiat.*, *117*:246, 1960.

Clark, L. C., Fox, R. P., Benington, F., Morin, R.: "Effect of mescaline, lysergic acid diethylamide, and related compounds on respiratory enzyme activity of brain homogenates." *Fed. Proc.*, *13*:27, 1954.

Cohen, G., Holland, B. and Goldenberg, M.: "Disappearance rates of infused epinephrine and norepinephrine from plasma." *A.M.A. Arch. gen. Psychiat.*, *1:*228, 1959.

Costa, E.: "The role of serotonin in neurobiology." *Intern. Rev. Neurobiol.*, *2:*137, 1960.

Costa, E. and Zetler, G.: "Interaction between epinephrine and some psychotimimetic drugs." *J. Pharm. Exp. Therap.*, *125:*230, 1959.

Curtis, D. R. and Koizumi, K.: "Chemical transmitter substances in brain stem of cat." *J. Neurophysiol.*, *24:*80, 1961.

Denber, H. C.: "Studies on mescaline. IX. Comparative action of various drugs on the mescaline-induced state." In *Biological Psychiatry*, Grune and Stratton, New York, 1959, p. 203.

Evarts, E. V.: "Neurophysiological correlates of pharmacologically-induced behavioral disturbances." *Assoc. Res. nerv. ment. Dis.*, *36:* 347, 1958.

Feldstein, A.: "On the relationship of adrenaline and its oxidation products to schizophrenia." *Amer. J. Psychiat.*, *116:*454, 1959.

Feldstein, A., Hoagland, H. and Freeman, H.: "On the relationship of serotonin to schizophrenia." *Science*, *128:*358, 1958.

Fessel, W. J.: "Disturbed serum proteins in chronic psychosis. Serological, Medical and psychiatric correlations." *A.M.A. Arch. gen. Psychiat.*, *4:*154, 1961.

Fessel, W. J. and Grunbaum, B. W.: "Electrophoretic and analytical ultracentrifuge studies in sera of psychotic patients: elevation of gamma globulins and macroglobulins, and splitting of alpha globulins." *Ann. int. Med.*, *54:*1134, 1961.

Fischer, E., Lagravere, T. A. F., Vazquez, A. J., Di Stefano, A. O.: "A bufotenin-like substance in the urine of schizophrenics." *J. Nerv. Ment. Dis.*, *133:*441, 1961.

Freedman, D. A., Sabshin, M., King, H. E. and O'Reardon, B.: "On the glucose tolerance test, and the effect on the formed elements of the blood of glucose and epinephrine in schizophrenia." *J. Nerv. Ment. Dis.*, *119:*31, 1954.

Freedman, D. X.: "Effects of LSD-25 on brain serotonin." *J. Pharm. Exp. Therap.*, *134:*160, 1961.

Freeman, H.: "Resistance to insulin in mentally disturbed soldiers." *A.M.A. Arch. Neurol. Psychiat.*, *56:*74, 1946.

Freeman, H.: "Schizophrenia: a review of the syndrome." In *Physiological Studies*, edited by L. Bellak and P. K. Benedict, New York, Logus Press, 1958.

Freeman, H. and Zaborenke, R. N.: "Relation of changes in carbohydrate metabolism to psychotic states." *A.M.A. Arch. Neurol. Psychiat.*, *61:* 569, 1949.

Friedhoff, A. J. and van Winkle, E.: "Isolation and characterization of a compound from the urine of schizophrenics." *Nature*, *194:*897, 1962.

Frohman, C. E., Latham, L. K., Beckett, P. G. S. and Gottlieb, J. S.: "Evidence of a plasma factor in schizophrenia." *A.M.A. Arch. gen. Psychiat.*, *2:*255, 1960a.

Frohman, C. E., Czajkowski, N. P., Luby, E. D., Gottlieb, J. S. and Senf, R.: "Further evidence of a plasma factor in schizophrenia." *A.M.A. Arch. gen. Psychiat.*, *2:*263, 1960b.

Frohman, C. E., Luby, E. D., Tourney, G., Beckett, P. G. S. and Gottlieb, J. S.: "Steps towards the isolation of a serum factor in schizophrenia." *Amer. J. Psychiat.*, *117:*401, 1960c.

Frohman, C. E.: In press, 1962.

Gaddum, J. H.: "Drugs antagonistic to 5-hydroxytryptamine." In *Ciba Foundation Symposium on Hypertension*, edited by G. E. W. Wolstenholme and M. P. Cameron, Boston, 1954.

Ganong, W. F., Goldfien, A., Halevy, A., Davidson, J. M. and Boryczka, A.: "Effect of lysergic acid diethylamide on adrenocortical and adrenal medullary function in the dog." *Acta. Endocrin.*, *37:*583, 1961.

Geiger, R. S.: "Effects of LSD-25, serotonin and sera from schizophrenic patients on adult mammalian brain cultures." *J. Neuropsychiat.*, *1:* 185, 1960.

German, G. A.: "Serum from schizophrenics and cortical potentials in the rat." *J. Physiol.*, *160:*10P, 1961.

Geronimus, L. H., Abramson, H. A. and Ingraham, L. J.: "Lysergic acid diethylamide (LSD-25): XXIII. Comparative effects of LSD-25 and related ergot drugs on brain tissue respiration and on human behavior." *J. Psychol.*, *42:*157, 1956.

Gessner, P. K.: "Disruption of the conditioned avoidance response of trained rats with 5-methoxy-N:N-dimethyltryptamine." *The Pharmacologist*, *3:*75, 1961.

Gildea, E. F., McLean, V. L. and Man, E. B.: "Oral and intravenous dextrose tolerance curves of patients with manic-depressive psychosis." *A.M.A. Arch. Neurol. Psychiat.*, *49:*852, 1943.

Gildea, E. F., Mailhouse, V. L. and Morris, D. P.: "The relationship between various emotional disturbances and the sugar content of the blood." *Amer. J. Psychiat.*, *92:*115, 1935.

Goodman, M., Luby, E. D., Frohman, C. E. and Gottlieb, J. S.: "Orosomucoid in schizophrenia." *Nature*, *192:*370, 1961.

Gottfried, S. P. and Willner, H. H.: "Blood chemistry of schizophrenic patients before, during and after insulin shock therapy." *A.M.A. Arch. Neurol. Psychiat.*, *62:*809, 1947.

Gottlieb, J. S., Frohman, C. E., Beckett, P. G. S., Tourney, G. and Senf, R.: "Production of high energy phosphate bonds in schizophrenia." *A.M.A. Arch. gen. Psychiat.*, *1:*243, 1959.

Grof, S., Vojtechovsky, M., Vitek, V. and Frankova, S.: "Clinical and experimental study of central effects of adrenochrome." *Abstracts IIIrd.* World Congress of Psychiatry, Montreal, 1961, p. 210.

Guth, P. S. and Sprites, M. A.: "Mode of action of chlorpromazine." *Biochem. Pharm.*, *8:*82, 1961.

Haavaldsen, R., Lingjaerde, O. and Walaas, O.: "Disturbances of carbohydrate metabolism in schizophrenics." *Confinia Neurologica*, *18:*270, 1958.

Hackfield, A. W.: "Are physiological disturbances related to the acute psychotic process in the mentally ill?" *A.M.A. Arch. Neurol. Psychiat.*, *28:*883, 1932.

Haddad, R. K. and Rabe, A.: "An anaphylactic test for abnormal antigen(s) in schizophrenic's serum". *Abstracts IIIrd. World Congress of Psychiatry*, Montreal, 1961, p. 608.

Harley-Mason, J., Laird, A. and Smythies, J. R.: "The metabolism of mescalin in the human." *Confinia Neurologica*, *18:*152, 1958.

Heim, R. and Hofmann, A.: "Isolment de la psilocybine a partir du 'Strophana Cubensis' Earle et d'autres espèces de champignons hallucinogènes mexicains appartenant au genre 'psilocybe'." *Compt. Rend. Acad. Sci.*, *247:*557, 1958.

Henneman, D. H., Altschule, M. D. and Goncz, R. M.: "Carbohydrate metabolism in brain disease. II. Glucose metabolism in schizophrenic, manic-depressive and involutional psychoses." *Arch. int. Med.*, *94:*402, 1954a.

Henneman, D. H., Altschule, M. D., Goncz, R. M. and Alexander, L.: "Carbohydrate metabolism in brain disease. I. Glucose metabolism in multiple sclerosis." *A.M.A. Arch. Neurol. Psychiat.*, *72:*688, 1954b.

Hoagland, H.: "A review of biochemical changes induced *in vivo* by lysergic acid diethylamide and similar drugs." *Ann. New York Acad. Sci.*, *66:*445, 1957.

Hoffer, A., Osmond, H. and Smythies, J. R.: "Schizophrenia. A new approach. Part II." *J. Ment. Sci.*, *100:*29, 1954.

Hollister, L. E.: "Clinical, biochemical and psychologic effects of psilocybin." *Arch. int. Pharmacodyn.*, *130:*42, 1961.

Holmberg, G. K., Greig, M. E. and Gibbons, A. J.: "The effect of sera of psychotic patients and control subjects on the uptake of C^{14} in the brains of mice after the injection of C^{14} glucose." *J. Neuropsychiat.*, *2:* 15, 1960.

Horwitt, M. K., Liebert, E., Kreisler, O. and Wittman, P.: *Bull. Natl. Research Council* (U.S.), No. 116, 1948.

Hoskins, R. G.: *The Biology of Schizophrenia.* New York, Norton, 1946.

Jourdan, F., Duchêne-Marullaz, P. and Boissier, P.: "Etude experimentale de l'action de la chlorpromazine sur le systeme nerveux végétatif." *Arch. int. Pharmacodyn.*, *101:*253, 1955.

Jus, A.: "Research on serum serotonin levels in acute psychotic states." *Neurologia, Neurochirurgia i Psychiatrica Polska.*, *11:*353, 1961.

Kerbikov, O. V.: "Immunological reactivity in schizophrenia as influenced by some modern drugs." *Ann. New York Acad. Sci.*, *92:*1098, 1961.

Kety, S. S.: "Biochemical theories of schizophrenia." *Science, 129:*1558-1590, 1959.

Key, B. J.: "The effect of chlorpromazine and lysergic acid diethylamide on conditioned avoidance responses." In *Neuropsychopharmacology.* Vol. 2, edited by E. Rothlin, Amsterdam, Elsevier, 1961, p. 158.

Key, B. J. and Bradley, P. B.: "The effect of drugs on conditioning and habituation to arousal stimuli in animals." *Psychopharmacologia, 1:*450, 1960.

Killam, K. F. and Killam, E. K.: "Action of lysergic acid diethylamide on central afferent and limbic pathways in cat." *J. Pharm. Exp. Therap.*, *116:*35, 1956.

Koch, P., Bordeleau, J. M. and Laurin, C.: "Corticoid induced phosphaturia in the schizophrenic and non-schizophrenic patient." *Canad. Psychiat. Assoc. J.*, *6:*45, 1961.

Kopin, I. J.: "Tryptophan loading and excretion of 5-hydroxyindoleacetic acid in normal and schizophrenic subjects." *Science, 129:*835, 1959.

Kuntzman, R., Costa, E., Gessa, G. L., Hirsch, C. and Brodie, B. B.: "Combined use of α-methyl meta-tyrosine (MMT) and reserpine to associate norepinephrine (NE) with excitation and serotonin (HT) with depression." *Fed. Proc., 20:*308, 1961.

La Brosse, E. H., Mann, J. D. and Kety, S. S.: "The physiological and psychological effects of intravenously administered epinephrine and its metabolism in normal and schizophrenic men. III. Metabolism of $7\text{-}H^3$-epinephrine as determined in studies of blood and urine." *J. Psychiat. Res., 1:*68, 1961.

Latham, K., Warner, K., Frohman, C. and Gottlieb, J.: "The effect of exercise on the serum factor in schizophrenic subjects." *Fed. Proc.*, *21:*415, 1962.

Le Blanc, J.: "Response to histamine in mental patients before and after tranquilizer therapy." *Biochem. Pharm.*, *8:*152, 1961.

Lenz, H.: "Papierchromatographische Untersuchungen des Harnes bei Schizophrenen und Geistesgesunden vor und nach Dopa-Verabreichung." *Psychopharmacologia*, *3:*146, 1962.

Lewis, J. L. and McIlwain, H.: "The action of some ergot derivatives, mescaline and dibenamine on the metabolism of separated mammalian cerebral tissues." *Biochem. J.*, *57:*680, 1954.

Lucy, J. D.: "Histamine tolerance in schizophrenia." *A.M.A. Arch. Neurol. Psychiat.*, *71:*629, 1954.

Ldueña, F. P.: "Sombre la farmacologia de la tricocereina, alcaloide del Trichocereus Terscheki (Parm.) Britton et Rose." *Rev. Soc. Argentina. Biol.*, *11:*604, 1935.

McIsaac, W. M.: "A biochemical concept of mental disease." *Postgrad. Med.*, *30:*111, 1961.

Maffii, G.: "Influenza della mescalina e della diethilamide dell'acido lisergico (LSD-25) sull'apprendimento del riflesso condizionato di salva guardia (primario e secondario) nel ratto." *Farmaco (Sci.)*, *14:*503, 1959.

Mahler, D. J. and Humoller, F. L.: "Effect of LSD and bufotenine on performance of trained rats." *Proc. Soc. exp. Biol. Med.*, *102:*697, 1959.

Meduna, L. J.: *Oneriöphrenia. The Confusional State.* Urbana, University of Illinois Press, 1950.

Meduna, L. J. and Vaichulis, J. A.: "A hyperglycaemic factor in the urine of so-called schizophrenics." *Dis. Nerv. Syst.*, *9:*248, 1948.

Meyerhof, O. and Randall, L. O.: "The inhibitory effects of adrenochrome on cell metabolism." *Arch. Biochem.*, *17:*171, 1948.

Morgan, M. S. and Pilgrim, F. J.: "Concentration of a hyperglycaemic factor from urine of schizophrenics." *Proc. Soc. exp. Biol. Med.*, *79:*106, 1952.

Moya, F., Dewar, J., MacIntosh, M., Hirsch, S. and Townsend, R.: "Hyperglycaemic action and toxicity of the urine of schizophrenic patients." *Can. J. Biochem. Physiol.*, *36:*505, 1958.

Olds, J.: "Self-stimulation in the brain." *Science*, *127:*315, 1958.

Örström, R.: "Isolation of phosphoglycolic acid from human erythrocytes." *Arch. Biochem. Biophys.*, *33:*484, 1951.

Örström, R. and Skaug, O.: "Isolation from blood of chronic schizophrenic patients of compounds active in radioactive phosphate turn-over." *Acta Psychiat. Neurol. Scand.*, *25:*437, 1950.

Osmond, H. and Smythies, J. R.: "Schizophrenia. A new approach." *J. Ment. Sci.*, *98:*309, 1952.

Park, J. H., Meriwether, B. P. and Park, C. R.: "Effects of adrenochrome on oxidative phosphorylation in liver mitochondria." *Fed. Proc.*, *15:* 141, 1956.

Pennes, H. H. and Hoch, P. H.: "Psychotomimetics, clinical and theoretical considerations. Harmine, Win 2299 and Nalline." *Amer. J. Psychiat.*, *113:*887, 1956.

Peretz, D., Smythies, J. R. and Gibson, W. C.: "A new hallucinogen. Trimethoxy-phenylisopropylamine." *J. Ment. Sci.*, *101:*317, 1955.

Pletscher, A. and Gey, K. F.: "Interference with permeation of aromatic monoamines and amino acids in brain, a possible new type of drug action." *Biochem. Pharm.*, *8:*82, 1961.

Pollin, W., Cardon, P. V., Jr. and Kety, S. S.: "Effects of amino acid feedings in schizophrenic patients treated with iproniazid." *Science*, *133:* 104, 1961.

Pollin, W. and Goldin, S.: "The physiological and psychological effects of intravenously administered epinephrine and its metabolism in normal and schizophrenic men—II. Psychiatric observations." *J. Psychiat. Res.*, *1:*50, 1961.

Price, J. M., Brown, R. R. and Peters, H. A.: "Tryptophan metabolism in porphyria, schizophrenia and a variety of neurologic and psychiatric diseases." *Neurology*, *9:*456, 1959.

Proctor, L. D., Dewar, J. G. and McNeel, B. H.: "Variations in the glucose tolerance observations in schizophrenics before and after shock treatment." *Amer. J. Psychiat.*, *100:*652, 1944.

Purpura, D. P.: "Electrophysiological analysis of psychotogenic drug action." *A.M.A. Arch. Neurol. Psychiat.*, *75:*122, 1956.

Quastel, J. H. and Wheatley, A. H. M.: "The effects of amines on oxidations of the brain." *Biochem. J.*, *27:*1609, 1933.

Radsma, W. and Golterman, H. L.: "The influence of adrenaline and adrenochrome on oxygen consumption of liver homogenates." *Biochim. Biophys. Acta.*, *13:*80, 1954.

Randall, L. O.: "The inhibition of the anaerobic glycolosis of rat brain by adrenochrome." *J. Biol. Chem.*, *165:*733, 1946.

Resnick, O., Wolfe, J. M., Freeman, H. and Elmadjian, F.: "Iproniazid treatment and metabolism of labelled epinephrine in schizophrenics." *Science*, *127:*1116, 1958.

Richter, D.: "Biochemical aspects of schizophrenia." In *Schizophrenia. Somatic Aspects*, edited by D. Richter, London, Pergamon Press, 1957.

Rinkel, M., Hyde, R. W., Solomon, H. C. and Hoagland, H.: "Experimental psychiatry. II. Clinical and physico-chemical observations in experimental psychosis." *Amer. J. Psychiat.*, *111*:881, 1955.

Rodnight, R.: "Body fluid indoles in mental illness." *Intern. Rev. Neurobiol.*, *3*:251, 1961.

Rodnight, R. and Aves, E. K.: "Body fluid indoles of normal and mentally-ill subjects." *J. Ment. Sci.*, *104*:1149, 1958.

Sacks, W.: "Cerebral metabolism of isotopic glucose in chronic mental disease." *J. applied Physiol.*, *14*:849, 1959.

Sankar, D. V. S., Gold, E. Phipps, E. and Sankar, D. B.: "Biochemical studies on schizophrenic children." *Abstracts IIIrd World Congress of Psychiatry*, Montreal, 1961a, p. 202.

Sankar, D. V. S., Gold, E. Phipps, E. Sankar, D. B.: "Effect of administration of lysergic acid diethylamide on serotonin levels in the body." *Nature*, *191*:499. 1961b.

Sawyer, C. H.: Discussion in *Ann. New York Acad. Sci.*, *66*:647, 1957.

Scheuler, F. W.: "The effect of succinate in mescaline hallucinations." *J. Lab. Clin. Med.*, *33*:1297, 1948.

Schopp, R. T., Kreutter, W. F. and Guzak, S. V.: "Neuromyal blocking action of mescaline." *Amer. J. Physiol.*, *200*:1226, 1961.

Shulgin, A. T., Bunnell, S. and Sargent, T.: "The psychotomimetic properties of 3,4,5-Trimethoxyamphetamine." *Nature*, *189*:1011, 1961.

Sigg, E. B. and Schneider, J. A.: "Mechanisms involved in the interaction of various central stimulants and reserpine." *E.E.G. Clin. Neurophysiol.*, *9*:419, 1957.

Simpson, G. M. and Kline, N. S.: "Histamine wheal formation and mental illness." *J. Nerv. Ment. Dis.*, *133*:19, 1961.

Smythies, J. R.: "Recent advances in the biochemistry of schizophrenia." *Lancet*, 1287, June 11, 1960.

Smythies, J. R., Koella, W. P. and Levy, C. K.: "The effect of mescalin on the optic evoked potentials in the unanesthetized rabbit." *J. Pharm. Exp. Therap.*, *129*:462, 1960.

Smythies, J. R. and Levy, C. K.: "The comparative psychopharmacology of some mescaline analogues." *J. Ment. Sci.*, *106*:531, 1960.

Spector, S., Bogdanski, D. F. and Brodie, B. B.: "Evidence that chlorpromazine exerts a generalized central sympatholytic action." *Fed. Proc.*, *16*:337, 1957.

Stevenson, I. and Sanchez, A. J.: "The antidotal effect of sodium succinate in the mescaline psychosis." *Amer. J. Psychiat.*, *114*:328, 1957.

Stevenson, J. A. F., Derrick, J. B., Hobbs, G. E. and Metcalfe, E. V.: "Adrenocortical response and phosphate excretion in schizophrenia." *A.M.A. Arch. Neurol. Psychiat.*, *78*:312, 1957.

Streifler, M. and Kornbluth, W.: "The effect of blood sera of schizophrenics on glucose utilization by the rat retina." in *Chemical Concepts of Psychosis*, edited by M. Rinkel and H. C. Denber, New York, McDowell/Obolensky. 1959

Szara, S., Axelrod, J. and Perlin, S.: "Is adrenochrome present in the blood?" *Amer. J. Psychiat.*, *115*:162, 1958.

Szara, S. and Rockland, L. H.: "Psychological effects and metabolism of N.N.-Diethyltryptamine—an hallucinogenic drug." *Abstracts IIIrd. World Congress of Psychiatry*, Montreal, 1961, p. 614.

Takahashi, Y. and Akabane, Y.: "Brain hexokinase activity." *A.M.A. Arch. gen. Psychiat.*, *3*:674, 1960.

Tsunoda, T. L.: "Effect of mescaline on respiration of cerebral tissue." *Folia Psychiat. Neurol. Jap.*, *14*:156, 1960.

Turner, W. J. and Mauss, E. A.: "Serotonin (5-hydroxytryptamine) and acetylcholine in human ventricular and spinal fluids." *A.M.A. Arch. Neurol. Psychiat.*, *81*:747, 1959.

Turner, W. J. and Merlis, S.: "Effect of some indolealkylamines on man." *A.M.A. Arch. Neurol. Psychiat.*, *81*:121, 1959.

Van Tamelen, E. E.: "The biogenesis of the ergot alkaloids." *Experentia*, *9*:457, 1953.

Vane, J. R.: "The actions of sympatheticomimetic amines on tryptamine receptors." In *Ciba Foundation Symposium on Adrenergic Mechanisms*, edited by J. R. Vane, London, Churchill, 1960.

Vogt, M.: "Drugs interfering with central actions of 5-hydroxytryptamine." In *5-hydroxytryptamine*, edited by G. P. Lewis, London, Pergamon Press, 1958, p. 209.

Von Taubmann, G. and Jantz, H.: "Untersuchung uber die dem Adenorchrom zugeschriebenen psychotoxischen Wirkungen." *Nervenarzt.*, *28*: 485, 1957.

Wada, J. and Gibson, W. C.: "Behavioral and EEG changes induced by injection of schizophrenic urine extract." *A.M.A. Arch. Neurol. Psychiat.*, *81*:747, 1959.

Walaszek, E. J.: "Brain neurohormones and cortical epinephrine pressor responses as affected by schizophrenic serum." *Intern. Rev. Neurobiol.*, *2*: 137, 1960.

Weckowicz, T. E. and Hall, R.: "Skin histamine reaction in schizophrenic and non-schizophrenic mental patients." *J. Nerv. Ment. Dis.*, *126*: 415, 1958.

Weil-Malherbe, H. and Liddell, D. W.: "Adrenaline and noradrenaline in cerebrospinal fluid." *J. Neurol.*, *17:*247, 1954.

Winter, C. A. and Flataker, L.: "Effect of blood plasma from psychotic patients upon performance of trained rats." *A.M.A. Arch. Neurol. Psychiat.*, *80:*441, 1958.

Wolbach, A. B., Jr., Isbell, H. and Miner, E. J.: "Cross tolerance between mescaline and LSD-25 with a comparison of the mescaline and LSD reactions." *Psychopharmacologia*, *3:*1, 1962.

Wood, H. G.: "Significance of alternate pathways in the metabolism of glucose." *Physiol. Rev.*, *35:*841, 1955.

Woolley, D. W. and Shaw, E.: "A biochemical and pharmacological suggestion about certain mental disorders." *Proc. Nat. Acad. Sci.*, *40:*228, 1954.

Zsigmond, E. K., Foldes, F. F. and Foldes, V. M.: "The *in vitro* inhibitory effect of LSD, its congeners and 5-hydroxytryptamine on human cholinesterases." *J. Neurochem.*, *8:*72, 1961.

ADDENDUM

In the interval between completing the galley proofs and the page proofs the following results have been reported that have a bearing on our theme.

1. Stewart and Irvine (1962) were unable to confirm Bishop's (1960) results on the effect of blood plasma from schizophrenic patients on conditioned avoidance reactions in the rat. They used chronic schizophrenics who had been off all drugs for two months and who had vitamin supplements to their diet. Their experimental design followed that of Bishop as closely as possible, yet they could show no difference between schizophrenic plasma, normal plasma and saline on the acquisition of the conditioned avoidance response. However, there were, in fact, two differences in the design: (i) Bishop stored his plasma for eight hours in the refrigerator whereas Stewart and Irvine used theirs fresh; (ii) Bishop records that his subjects were given regular exercise, whereas Stewart and Irvine do not mention this parameter, which is clearly vital in all such studies following the demonstration by Latham *et al.* (1962) that schizophrenic plasma is active in their tests only following a certain amount of exercise.

2. Recently a report from Russia (Lando *et al.*, 1962) gives support to previous claims that blood HT is raised in schizophrenia (and epilepsy) but only in certain cases.

3. Huszak and Durko (1962) have studied indole excretion patterns and metabolism in schizophrenics. They claim that *mean* values of 5-hydroxy-IAA excretion levels in the urine do not distinguish between schizophrenics and normals but that *median* levels do, and schizophrenics show higher values and more hourly variation.

A tryptophane load made no difference in either case on 5-hydroxy-IAA levels but, using chromatographic methods, they claimed that the IAA spot got larger following a tryptophane load, whereas this did not happen in the case of the schizophrenics. This may correlate with the findings of Price *et al* (1959) that schizo-phrenics tend to use preferentially the kynurenine pathway.

4. Weil-Malherbe *et al*. (1962) and Fujita (1962) were unable to confirm Walaszek's claims concerning the effect of schizophrenic serum on brain amines and on the cortical epinephrine pressor response.

5. In the field of the model psychoses, Gessner and Page (1962) have published a report on the behavioral effects of tryptamine derivatives and correlated these with their lipid solubility (by determining chloroform/water partition coefficients.) There was a rough correlation between a drug's psychotropic action and its partition coefficient. In particular LSD had much the highest coefficient (76) and bufotenin and HT the lowest (0.67, 0.62). Other values were tryptamine and DMT 2, DET 17 and 5-me-thoxy DMT 6.4.

Weiss *et al*. (1962) report the interesting finding that dimethyl acetamide—$CH_3.CO.N(CH_3)_2$—if given in a dosage of 400mg./kg. daily for 3 days or more—produces a toxic confusional state plus hallucinations and mild or severe confusion. Thus it appears to be a deliriant rather than a psychoto-mimetic drug (because it in-duces confusion—but a smaller dose might not). However its chem-ical formula is of great interest in relation to those of DMT, bufo-tenin, psilocybin, etc.

Lastly Sai-Halász (1962) has claimed that pretreatment with the most potent anti-HT agent known (1-methyl-D-lysergic acid butanolamide—UML-491) potentiates the psychotomimetic effect (in humans) of DMT. A dose of DMT of 0.35mg./kg. (which normally has no psychotomimetic effect) produced such an effect in 8 subjects pretreated with UML-491. A dosage of 0.81-0.89mg./ kg. (which had induced a moderate psychotomimetic reaction in the same subjects 2 - 3 months earlier) produced much more intense psychic symptoms after UML-491. The author suggests therefore that DMT effects may be exerted via brain HT to some degree.

6. Yuwiler (1962) in a carefully controlled study has failed to detect any differences between schizophrenics and controls in the excretion rates of "aminochromes" (expressed as substances pre-cipitated by lead from acidified urine). Thus the claim of Veech

et al. (1961) that schizophrenics excrete excess "aminochromes" has not been confirmed. Yuwiler suggests that their control population was inadequate.

REFERENCES FOR ADDENDUM

Gessner, P. K. and Page, I. H.: "Behavioral effects of 5-methoxy-N: N-dimethyl tryptamine, other tryptamines and LSD." *Amer. J. Physiol.*, *203:167*, 1962.

Fujita, S.: In discussion in *Ann. N. Y. Acad. Sci.*, *96:*423, 1962

Huszak, I. and Durko, I.: "The metabolism of indole compounds in schizophrenia." *Psychiat. Neurol. (Basel)*, *143:*407, 1962.

Lando, L. I., Zakhaviane, Y. L. and Kroupenina, L. B.: "The content of serotonin in the blood in mental illness and its modification during treatment." *Zh. Nevropat. Psychiat. Korsakov*, *62,:*99, 1962.

Sai-Halász, A.: "The effect of antiserotonin on the experimental psychosis induced by dimethyltryptamine." *Experentia*, *18:*137, 1962.

Stewart, C. N. and Irvine, D. G.: "The effect of blood plasma from schizophrenic patients on avoidance conditioning in the rat." *Dis. Nerv. Syst.*, *23:*456, 1962.

Veech, R. L., Bigelow, L. B., Denckla, W. D., Altschule, M. D.: "Urinary aminochromes in schizophrenia." *A.M.A. Arch. Gen. Psychiat.* *5:*127, 1961.

Weil-Malherbe, H., Posner, H. S. and Waldrop, F. N.: "The alleged effect of schizophrenic serum on rabbit brain catecholamines." *Ann. N. Y. Acad. Sci.*, *96:*419, 1962.

Weiss, A. J., Mancall, E. L., Koltes, J. A., White, J. C. and Jackson, L. G.: "Dimethylacetamide. A hitherto unrecognized hallucinogenic agent." *Science*, *136:*151, 1962.

Yuwiler, A.: "Urinary aminochromes and mental illness." *J. Nerv. Ment. Dis.*, *135:*365, 1962.

AUTHOR INDEX

SUBJECT INDEX

Note for Using This Index

a. refers to direct studies on schizophrenic patients and their metabolism.

b. refers to the effect of plasma (or other body fluids) from schizophrenic patients on some biological or biochemical test system.

c. refers to an hallucinogenic drug or drugs (this is not used where this is obvious, i.e., under the hallucinogenic drugs themselves).

d. refers to an agent used to test schizophrenic metabolism.

e.g.: Bufotenin (a): refers to reports to have isolated this compound in schizophrenic body fluids.

Bufotenin (c): refers to properties of bufotenin as an hallucinogen.

Evoked potentials (b): refers to effect of schizophrenic plasma on these in some animal brain.

Evoked potentials (c): refers to effect of hallucinogenic drugs on these in some animal brain.

83